Troubleshooting Home Automation

A Complete Guide to Diagnosing and Solving Power Line Carrier Problems

Jeff Fisher

Approaching, Inc.
San Jose, California, USA.

Library of Congress Cataloging in Publication Data

Troubleshooting Home Automation: A Complete Guide to Diagnosing and Solving Power Line Carrier Problems

Jeff Fisher.

p. cm.

ISBN 1-881911-02-0 (soft cover)

1. Electronics

Ménage is a registered trademark of Ménage Automation, Inc.

DECORA and DECORA ELECTRONIC CONTROLS are trademarks of Leviton Manufacturing Co., Inc.

POWERFLASH, POWERHOUSE, PROTECTOR PLUS, and X-10 are trademarks of X-10 (USA), Inc.

Library of Congress Card Catalog Number 97-073374

Cover design by Brian Maggi.

Illustrations by Jeff Fisher and Brian Maggi.

Printed in the United States of America

Preface

Since 1992 I have sold power line carrier products to everyone from electrical contractors to senior citizens. Most install the equipment themselves and have no trouble at all. Some either come in or call with simple questions or problems relating to operation. A few have problems with equipment that is defective (which is cheerfully and immediately replaced). And then there are the handful with problems that cannot be solved in the store or over the phone. The resulting service calls represent the "worst of the worst" problems out of thousands of installations.

It is for someone facing this type of situation that this book was written.

The last thing I want this book to do is to scare anyone away from using power line carrier (PLC) equipment in an otherwise reasonable situation. Quite the contrary, I believe the mere existence of this book should help you feel more willing to use PLC products. You have, in this book, the distilled knowledge of someone that has been through situations much worse than you will probably experience.

I would like to thank Skyler Waite of **Lightscapes** in Atherton, California for his patience while I performed an exorcism on a client's home. And for letting me pick his brain during the creation of this book. I'd also like to thank John Lockyer of Home Automation Systems who reviewed the text and provided many helpful suggestions.

Every effort was made to assure the information in this book is correct. If you find an error or omission, let us know, and we'll fix it in the next printing; however, we make no guarantee nor assume any liability beyond the cover price of this book.

Throughout the book, you'll occasionally see paragraphs like this one with a line above and below, and one of the two symbols shown at the left. The upper symbol, an exclamation point within a triangle, points out a dangerous situation. You should always read and follow these warnings very carefully. Paragraphs with the lower symbol, an "i" in a circle, indicate a paragraph that provides a more detailed explanation of a concept, or more detailed information about a procedure or situation.

WARNING! Always remember that household voltages are potentially lethal. Observe all precautions when working with home wiring. Specifically, *never* rewire "live" circuitry. Always turn off the appropriate breaker(s) before disconnecting or connecting any wires. If you need to measure voltages, prepare for the measurement with the power off, turn the breaker on and measure, then turn the breaker back off.

If you are in any way uncomfortable with any aspect of the task at hand, call a licensed electrician.

If you are not familiar with all Federal, State, and Local wiring codes when installing new wiring and fixtures, call a licensed electrician. Improper wiring can pose a fire and safety threat. If you are not absolutely sure that you know what you're doing, consult an electrician. Household electricity can be lethal.

This book is designed to be a practical guide to fixing problems. Each chapter defines a situation and drives through a step-by-step method to solving the problem. If you spend a lot of time working on power line carrier equipment, it would behoove you to read this book from cover to cover for the type of overview that will be useful in complex problem analysis. For simple problems, the table of contents and index will quickly move you to the chapter needed to fix the issue.

Good luck.

Contents

1 Start Here

"In the beginning God created the heavens and the earth. The earth was without form and void, and darkness was upon the face of the deep; and the Spirit of God was moving over the face of the waters. And God said, "Let there be light"; and there was light."

—Book of Genesis, revised standard version.

To Fix a Specific Problem

You can use this book to determine and correct a specific power line carrier (**PLC**) problem. Look through the chapter headings in the table of contents for the first entry that reasonably matches any symptom you are seeing. Go to that chapter and follow all directions.

If that fails to identify and correct the problem, go back to the table of contents and try the next chapter that most nearly matches. If you run out of chapters before you fix the problem, and you're sure you correctly followed all directions, then—congratulations—you've just discovered a previously unknown problem. We would be very interested in working to resolve the problem and to add its detection and resolution to this book. Please send a description of the problem to us at our electronic mail address: info@approaching.com.

To Learn How To Troubleshoot PLC

If you wish to become an instant expert in troubleshooting PLC problems, read this book from cover to cover. This will indoctrinate you with all known symptoms and problems, and with their resolution. Please accept, in advance, my sympathies since the topic and the required "just-the-facts-ma'am" presentation leaves little room for entertainment value.

Older Equipment

Many times I've listened to customers complain about unusual behavior by a module. In response, I always ask for an exact description of the symptoms. If the symptom is that the light mysteriously comes on by itself, I also ask how long they've had the module. Invariably they've had the module many years. Early **X-10** modules were dark brown in color. Later modules are light beige or white. There are many design differences between the old and new modules.

One characteristic of the older modules (I call them "LBM's" for Little Brown Modules) was that they were susceptible to false triggering. This could cause lights and appliances on modules to turn on unexpectedly. This often coincided with power line surges and sags, either from the mains or from local high-current equipment turning on or off.

My experience also indicates that older modules were somewhat less "sensitive" to PLC signals because they require a stronger signal than the newer modules.

So, before spending a lot of time troubleshooting PLC problems, consider replacing those ancient modules. This could save a lot of time and effort.

Common Failure Modes

After several years of troubleshooting, I've noticed some "common failure modes" with PLC devices (see Table 1, "Most Frequently Seen Failures," on page 3). This isn't to say that certain devices fail more often, but that when they do fail, it's usually in the manner stated. I present this information simply to assist your troubleshooting, since solving the problem sometimes comes down to a "best guess" about which of one or more pieces has failed. If the symptoms match a particular device's common failure mode, you can make an "educated guess" rather than a blind one.

First of all, my experience has shown that Leviton products have far fewer failures than do X-10 products. Again, this isn't to say that X-10 products have excessive failures, just that Leviton has fewer.

Next, all **incandescent** wall switches and lamp modules (X-10 part numbers WS467, WS477, and LM465, or Leviton part numbers 6381-WI, 6383-WI, and 6376) contain a device called a **triac**. The triac has a common failure mode that causes the lamp(s) to "flicker." The light may even go off and on by itself. In extreme cases, this can lead to the infamous "haunted house" effect. If a lamp flickers the cause is probably the triac in the wall switch.

Table 1 provides some additional common failure modes for other PLC devices that can help in troubleshooting.

Table 1: Most Frequently Seen Failures

Model Number	Description	Common Failure Mode
6291-WI	Wall Switch Relay Module Only very old versions of this device (can be identified by a completely flat pushpanel with tabs on each side)	Chatters when turned on either locally or remotely. Gradually gets worse until unable to turn load on at all.
6381-WI 6383-WI	Incandescent Wall Switch Module	Bulbs flicker or won't come on at all. Usually a bad triac. Sometimes occurs when the bulb burns out, causing a current surge.
PR511	Dual Floodlight Motion Detector	Total failure. Power supply seems to burn out. Lights may be stuck "on" or "off" and cannot be controlled.
TM751	RF Transceiver Portion of Remote Control System	Reduced range. Sometimes within hours, sometimes after several days. Range may reduce to mere inches.
WS467	Wall Switch Module	After many years of use, the contacts behind the button can wear out, making it hard to turn the light on or off.

2 Wall Switches That Won't

"Strong men know not despair...for this wins neither heaven nor earth. Throw off this ignoble discouragement, and arise like a fire that burns all before it."

—the Bhagavad Ghita

Use this chapter to troubleshoot wall switches that fail to operate the lights from the local wall switch module. If the local switch works properly, but the switch doesn't respond to some or all remote commands, see Chapter 3, "Missed Commands," on page 11.

Is the Cutoff Switch Turned Off?

If the switch is an X-10 WS467 or WS477 or Leviton 6381-WI, 6381-UWI, 6383-WI, or 6383-UWI, and the load will not turn on at all, slide the small **cutoff switch** located just below the button or press panel all the way to the right.

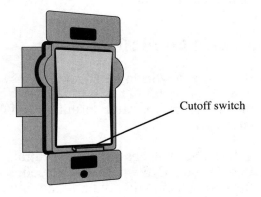

Cutoff switch

Figure 1. Cutoff Operation on Leviton-style Switch

Why? These switches turn their loads on and off with a solid state component rather than with physical contacts. Underwriters' Laboratories, Inc. requires a physical contact in the switch to cut off the current while servicing the load. This slide switch can sometimes be turned off by accident, keeping the load permanently off.

Are the Line and Load Wired Correctly?

If this is a new installation, turn off power, disconnect the switch's black and blue leads (or **LOAD** and **LINE** screw terminals), and secure the two wires from the wall box together using a wire-nut.

 Warning! If there are four wires in the switch box, it is absolutely critical that you connect the same color wires together (black to black and white to white). If you are ever unsure of what you are doing, hire a licensed electrician.

Turn the breaker back on. If the load does not come on, there is something wrong somewhere else in the wiring or the load.

Why? Switch modules connect, either electronically or physically, these two wires together to turn the load on. If physically connecting these two wires doesn't turn on the load, the wall switch won't be able to either. If this is a three- or four-way installation, there may be a wiring mistake in another box that is depriving this box of a LINE. Refer to Chapter 5, "Three- and Four-Way Switch Wiring."

If connecting these two wires turns on the load, re-connect the switch and continue.

Are the Line and Load Reversed?

If this is a new installation and if the switch is a Leviton 6291-WI, 6381-UWI, 6293-WI, or 6383-UWI, try reversing the connections to the black wire (or LINE terminal) and the blue wire (or LOAD terminal).

Why? The switches without a neutral connection do not care if the LOAD and LINE wires are reversed, but these switches do. Reversing them will not harm the switch, but the switch will not operate properly either.

If this does not solve the problem, restore the original wiring and continue.

No Neutral Connection?

If this is a new installation and if the switch is a Leviton 6291-WI, 6381-UWI, 6293-WI, or 6383-UWI, turn off the breaker, disconnect the white lead (or **NEUTRAL** terminal), *temporarily* connect the white lead (or NEUTRAL terminal) to the nearest ground. (Perhaps a nearby grounded outlet's ground hole.) Turn the breaker on and test the switch.

Why? These switches use the neutral wire to power their electronics. Switches without a neutral wire "trickle" a small amount of current through the load to derive their power. With or without a neutral wire, the power consumption is less than two watts. If the switch requires a neutral connection, and the neutral connection is bad, the switch will not operate. A ground will function, *for testing purposes only*, as a substitute for a neutral.

If the switch works this way, determine what is wrong with the neutral in your box and reconnect. If the switch doesn't work, reconnect the white wire to the neutral and go to the next step.

Is the Control Wired Incorrectly?

If this is a new installation, and you're using a three- or four-way switch (X-10 model WS477, or Leviton 6293-WI, 6383-WI, or 6383-UWI), double-check all wiring (see Chapter 5, "Three- and Four-Way Switch Wiring"). If the switch passed the test in the section labeled "Are the Line and Load Wired Correctly?" on page 6, disconnect the red wire (or **CONTROL**) terminal. Try the switch module now. (The slave switches don't work.)

Why? The red wire (or control terminal) provides the "signal" from the slave switch(es) when they are pressed. If the slave switches are wired incorrectly, the control signal may be "active" all the time, keeping the main switch from working.

If the master switch works now, there is something wrong with your slave switch wiring. When properly connected, the control line should be **floating** unless a slave switch is pressed, then the control line should be momentarily connected to a LINE.

Is the Load "Wired Hot"?

If this is a new installation, and you're using a Leviton 6291-WI, 6381-UWI, 6293-WI, or 6383-UWI, disconnect the blue wire or

LOAD screw terminal. Then, at the load, (light fixture, florescent ballast, fan connection, etc.), see if the black wire is still "hot" (has line voltage.)

Why? Occasionally a switch and load is wired incorrectly in the first place. The most common, and dangerous, is the "wired hot" fixture. This is where the line is connected to the load, and the other side of the load is brought to the switch. This "post load line" is then switched to the neutral.

If the black wire at the load is still hot, and you have one of the above type switches, no amount of juggling the switch wires will allow the use of X-10 or Leviton products. Rewire the light in the proper manner.

Is the Switch Button Sticking?

If the switch is a Leviton 6381-WI, 6383-WI, 6381-UWI, or 6383-UWI, verify that the tab of the cutoff switch is pointing *away* from the touch plate (see Figure 2).

Why? If the tab of the cutoff switch is pointing towards the touch plate, it can bind the moving parts. This can cause the light to brighten and dim continuously.

Make sure this isn't your problem. If you had difficulty getting the switch into the box, you may have warped the front plate. If this is the case, you may need to do a little carving on the touch plate to get it to operate freely.

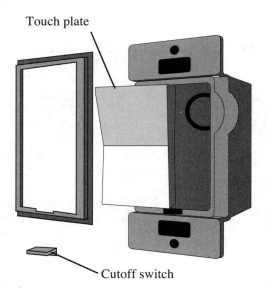

Figure 2. Decora Style Switch

Is the Triac Bad?

If the switch is a Leviton 6381-WI, 6383-WI, 6381-UWI, or 6383-UWI, and the load flickered before failing, or the load goes on and off by itself, replace the switch.

Why? The electronic part inside the switch that controls the load in these modules is called a triac. When this part fails it can operate sporadically, flashing the light. The triacs sometimes "blow" when a bulb burns out, causing a current surge. This is more likely if there is a single high-wattage bulb, or when the load is greater than 500 watts.

This doesn't happen often, but it is the most common failure mode of these switches.

Is it the Wrong Type of Switch?

Using the formulas and tables in Chapter 6, "Module And Controller Specifications," verify that you have the proper switch module for the load, and that the load is not greater than the rating of the switch. Change the switch, if necessary.

 Remember to consider the total wattage for the load. For example, if you are switching an incandescent lamp with three 60-watt bulbs, the total load is 180 watts (plus an inrush factor, see Chapter 6).

Why? Switch modules are designed for specific types of loads, and have maximum ratings. The wrong type of switch, or too large a load, can cause premature failure of the switch module.

Is Something Else Wrong With the Switch?

If none of the preceding steps has solved the problem, replace the switch module. (Or swap it with another to see if the problem follows the module.)

Why? It's very rare, but even **relay** switches can fail.

3 Missed Commands

"What the king fundamentally insisted upon was that his authority should be respected. He tolerated no disobedience. He was an absolute monarch. But, because he was a very good man, he made his orders reasonable. His rule was not only absolute: it was also universal.

'And the stars obey you?'

'Certainly they do,' the king said.'They obey instantly. I do not permit insubordination.'"

—Antoine de Saint-Exupery, *The Little Prince*

Use this section if modules do not consistently respond to your controller's commands.

PLC Signal Transmission Problems

The most common problems with power line carrier installations are modules that do not reliably respond to controllers. Other than broken or incorrectly installed equipment, there are two possible reasons for these problems: low **signal strength**, and **noise**.

PLC signals measure over 2 volts at the controller. Many things eat away at the strength of this signal as it spreads throughout the wiring structure. The signal strength must be above 50 millivolts (50mV is 0.050 volts) by the time it reaches a module for the module to detect the signal. Many things can have a small effect on signal transmission, including what appliances are on and off, what your utility company is doing, and even the weather. I recommend that you have a signal strength of at least 100mV at each module. This way, minor variations in signal strength usually do not reduce the signal strength below the 50mV threshold.

PLC signals can be "masked" by noise on the power line. There are all kinds of noise, but for noise to affect PLC it must have some 120 Khz component to it, and it must occur at the AC **zero crossing point**. Many appliances put noise on the power line but—fortunately—few do so at exactly 120Khz and at the zero crossing point. For example, Lutron dimmer switches create a massive amount of 120 Khz noise, but do not affect PLC because none of the noise is at the zero crossing point.

For an overview of X-10 components and how they work together, see Appendix B. To understand X-10 signals and how they're transmitted, see Appendix C.

User Error?

If your controller *never* operates the module, make sure all the switches are set correctly (same Housecode letter, same Unit Code number.) All plug-in controllers have some sort of indicator light so that you can tell if they are receiving AC.

Also make sure that users understand that, for instance, to turn on light 13 from a maxi-controller (X-10 model SC503), they should press "13" and "ON", not "1", "3", and "ON". Sounds silly, but I've received more than one call on this.

 Housecode and Unit Code dials can sometimes be slightly out of alignment. Before assuming you have a more serious problem, try changing the dials on your module to be sure they are set properly.

Is the Resistance of the Load Too High?

If the module that operates unreliably is an incandescent module (X-10 WS467, WS4777, or Leviton 6381-WI, or 6383-WI) and you have a single quartz bulb or a small (less than 60W) regular bulb, either replace the bulb with a non-quartz bulb, replace the module with a universal version (Leviton 6381-UWI or 6383-UWI), or replace the module with a relay version (Leviton 6291-WI, or 6293-WI).

Why? The resistance of a single quartz bulb when off is much higher than a non-quartz bulb. Sometimes this resistance is so high that the module cannot "bleed" enough current through the bulb to operate. The symptom is (usually) that you can turn the light off, but you can't turn it back on. This may only happen after the light has cooled down. The universal and relay modules draw their power through a neutral connection so this isn't a problem.

Is This an RF Problem?

Some controllers, like the X-10 Wireless Transceiver, first send commands via **radio frequency** (RF) to a transceiver module (X-10 part number TM751) that forwards the commands across the house's electrical wiring. If you're using a wireless transceiver, make sure this isn't a radio transmission problem by unplugging the transceiver (X-10 TM751, RR501, or Leviton 6314) and using a plug-in controller to operate the modules.

Why? This document deals with problems related to power line carrier signals being sent over your house electrical wiring. RF transmission problems can vary widely and are beyond the scope of this book.

Procedure for Localizing the Problem

The most important skill to develop in troubleshooting PLC problems is the ability to quickly narrow down the problem to the offending device(s) or area. Like many skills, this one involves tools. You will need the Leviton Test Set Transmitter (Leviton part number 6385) and Test Set Receiver (Leviton part number 6386). You can purchase or rent these devices at your home automation reseller. If you are determined to get by without these tools, you can skip this procedure and go through the rest of this chapter trying things until you hit on a solution. Be warned, however, that this may be the most time-consuming solution in the long run.transitory

Warning! If you are not completely comfortable working in a "live" **circuit breaker** box, do not attempt this procedure. Instead, call an electrician. Household electrical wiring can be lethal.

This procedure starts at the very beginning, adding one "piece" of your home wiring at a time until the problem area surfaces. It then narrows down that area until you find a problem. You may need to repeat this procedure more than once to find multiple problems. Once you have been through this procedure a few times, you may elect to "start in the middle and work out." This may be faster, but only if you know what you're doing.

If the house has **sub panels**, perform the procedure on the **main panel** first, treating each sub-panel as a single circuit. Then perform the whole procedure on each sub-panel.

Make sure there are no computers in the middle of processing something, VCR's recording, and so on. (You'll be turning off all the power.) You'll need the Automatic Test Transmitter, the Signal Strength Indicator, and the test cord (see "Test Cord" on page 70). You may also need a flashlight.

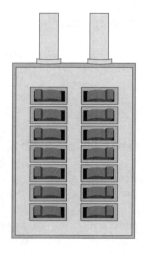

Figure 3. Typical Breaker Box

Remove the cover from the main breaker box. Turn off all breakers.

 Even though all the breakers are turned off, the main terminals are still hot. A circuit breaker box is very dangerous. If you are not a licensed electrician, you should hire one to complete this phase of troubleshooting.

Plug both the Automatic Test Transmitter and the Signal Strength Indicator into the Test Cord. Carefully clip one lead onto the neutral in the breaker box.

The neutral is a metal bar with many screw terminals and many white wires connected. For information about test equipment, see Appendix A.

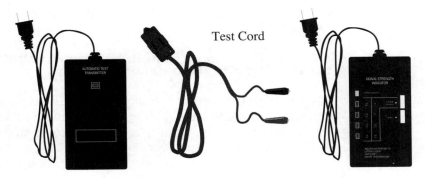

Test Cord

Figure 4. Test Equipment.

Very carefully and without touching it with your fingers connect the other lead to one of the main hot terminals.

A large black wire connects to each of these terminals. If you have standard residential split-phase wiring, you have two of these terminals. If there are three of these terminals (in addition to the neutral), you have three-phase wiring. (Sometimes found in apartments and condos, often found in commercial buildings.)

Press and hold the HI RANGE button on the Signal Strength Indicator.

It should indicate 2v. Note that it may take a second or two for the indicators to stabilize. If the ERROR light comes on, press the RESET button momentarily. If it comes back on, see the section "Do You Have Noise on Your Power Line?" on page 23. If you have less than 2v indicated, there is something wrong with your test set, so you'll need to get a new one before continuing.

Repeat this step for each additional main hot terminal. Both (split-phase) or all three (three-phase) main hot terminals should show 2V and no ERROR. Congratulations, your power is clean. The problem must be inside the house.

Now that you know the problem is inside the house, you can use the Automatic Test Transmitter to send signals back to the breaker box, where you measure them with the Signal Strength Indicator.

You want to send the test signals from the same outlet your controller uses.

Unplug a controller that is having problems transmitting and replace it with the Automatic Test Transmitter; then, turn on the breaker for that circuit.

Leave all of the other breakers off. If this is a sub-panel and the transmitter is not on one of these breakers, turn all the sub-panel breakers off.

Measure the signal strength between neutral and each of the main hots in the breaker box.

The hot with the highest signal strength will be the phase that is connected to the test transmitter. This should read at least 500mV, allowing for a 75 percent drop in signal strength from the transmitter to the breaker box. If the signal strength reads less than 500mV, see the section titled "Surge Suppression Soaking up the Signal?" on page 19 and the section "Is an Appliance Soaking up the Signal?" on page 20. If the ERROR light comes on, see the section "Is an Appliance Inside Creating Noise?" on page 22.

Without changing the test setup, begin turning on all the breakers on the same phase (see Figure 5) and all 220V breakers (they look like two breakers with their handles tied together).

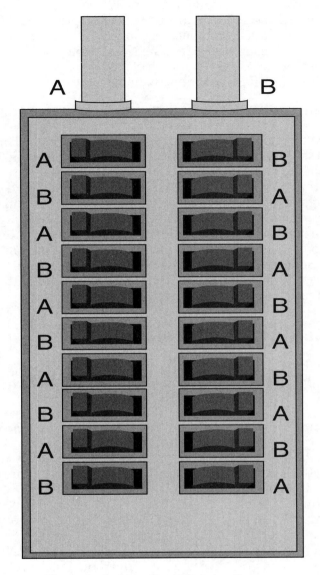

Figure 5. Inside a Circuit Breaker Box

Watch the signal strength light go on and off at least twice between each new breaker. If the signal strength drops noticeably (especially if it drops below 250mV), something on the last turned-on circuit is soaking up the PLC signal. See the section "Surge Suppression Soaking up the Signal?" on page 19, and the section "Is an

Appliance Soaking up the Signal?" on page 20. If the error light refuses to stay extinguished when you press RESET, something on the last turned-on branch is causing PLC noise. See the section "Is an Appliance Inside Creating Noise?" on page 22. If all the breakers on that phase are ON, you have at least 500mV of signal strength, and no ERROR, continue with the next step.

Turn on all the electronic equipment that has power.

At this point, only half of your breakers are on. This includes computers, printers, copiers, stereo amps, TVs, lights on non-PLC dimmers (set dimmers to 50percent), and so on. If the signal level drops noticeably, one of the appliances you turned on is soaking up signal. See the section "Surge Suppression Soaking up the Signal?" on page 19 and the section "Is an Appliance Soaking up the Signal?" on page 20. If the ERROR light now comes on, one of the appliances you turned on is generating PLC noise, see the section "Is an Appliance Inside Creating Noise?" on page 22. If you still have at least 500mV and no ERROR, continue to the next step to see if the signal is "bridging" phases properly.

Connect the test lead of the Signal Strength Indicator to the other main hot in the breaker box.

If the signal strength is less than 250mV, allowing for a 50 percent drop between phases, you have a bridging problem. See the section "Do You Have "Side-itus"?" on page 21.

Turn on the remaining breakers one at a time.

If the signal strength drops noticeably (especially if it drops below 250mV) something on the last turned-on circuit is soaking up the PLC signal. See the section "Surge Suppression Soaking up the Signal?" on page 19 and the section "Is an Appliance Soaking up the Signal?" on page 20. If the ERROR light comes on, something on the last turned-on branch is causing PLC noise. See the section "Is an Appliance Inside Creating Noise?" on page 22. If all the breakers are on and you have at least 250mV of signal strength and no ERROR, continue with the next step.

Turn on all remaining electronic equipment.

If the signal level drops noticeably, one of the appliances you turned on is soaking up signal. See the section "Surge Suppression Soaking up the Signal?" on page 19, and the section "Is an Appliance Soaking up the Signal?" on page 20. If the ERROR light now comes on, one of the appliances you turned on is generating PLC noise. See the section "Is an Appliance Inside Creating Noise?" on page 22. If you still have at least 250mV of signal strength and no ERROR, continue to the next step to see if the signal is making it out to the receiver.

Connect the Signal Strength Indicator in place of the module that is having problems receiving the PLC commands.

If the level reads less than 100mV (or doesn't read at all), something on this circuit is soaking up the signal. See the section "Surge Suppression Soaking up the Signal?" on page 19, and the section "Is an Appliance Soaking up the Signal?" on page 20. If the ERROR light is on, something on this branch is creating noise. See the section "Is an Appliance Inside Creating Noise?" on page 22. If the signal reads 50mV or more, everything is fine.

Surge Suppression Soaking up the Signal?

Plug-in controllers and modules should *never* be plugged into power-strips with built-in surge-suppression. Also, try to limit the number of surge-suppression power-strips in your home.

Why? The circuitry used by cheap surge-suppression power-strips tends to "soak up" the powerline carrier signal. The closer, electrically, the surge-suppression is to the controller or module, the more signal will be soaked up. The experts assure me that cheap surge-suppression power-strips are virtually worthless as protection anyway. Also, high-end "sine-wave tracking" whole-house surge suppression systems can suppress PLC signals. If you are truly worried about surges, Leviton makes whole-house surge suppression systems that are compatible with PLC signals.

Are Extension Cords Soaking up the Signal?

Plug-in controllers (X-10 part numbers MC460, SC503, SD533, MT522, PF284, TR551, TW523, and CP290, and Leviton part number 6325), and transceivers (X-10 TM751 and RR501 and Leviton 6314) should be directly plugged in to the wall outlet for strongest signal transmission.

Why? Placing a controller at the end of a long, light-gauge extension cord reduces the signal strength considerably. This is especially true if there are other loads on the extension cord.

Is an Appliance Soaking up the Signal?

Identify which appliance on a circuit is soaking up the signal by unplugging, one at a time, each appliance. When the signal strength increases, you've found the culprit. Isolate this appliance with a plug-in noise suppressor (Leviton 6288).

Don't just turn off the appliances—unplug them. Most appliances have their filters before the power switch and many still draw some power even when off.

Why? Designers sometimes put too much filtering on the AC line coming into their products. See the section "Surge Suppression Soaking up the Signal?" on page 19.

Do You Have "Side-itus"?

If some modules work from some locations, but not others, the

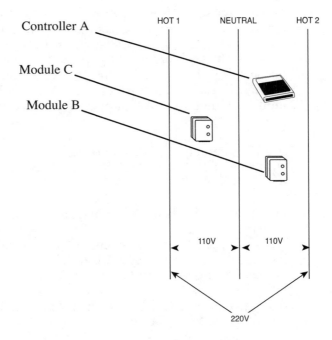

Controller A

Module C

Module B

HOT 1   NEUTRAL   HOT 2

110V   110V

220V

Figure 6.   Standard Split-Phase
Residential Wiring

signal may be having difficulty crossing from one "side" of your
split-phase wiring to another. This is what I call "side-itus." The
problem can be solved by installing a Leviton signal bridge (part
number 6299).

Why? A PLC signal starts out at 2 volts, and *may* operate a module
with as little as 0.025 volts. At least 0.1 volt (100mV) or more of
signal strength is required for reliable operation. Many things
degrade the signal along the way, but the biggest drop is usually
between **phases.** (See Figure 6.) In standard split-phase residential
wiring, controller A can transmit to module B quite easily since it's
on the same phase. But controller A and module C only have one
wire in common. It's tough to push a current without a return path!
In practice, many things allow the signal to seep onto the other phase
(220 volt appliances, the utilities' power transformer, etc.). If one
side of your house is "invisible" from the other (PLC speaking), you
can solve this with a Leviton signal bridge (part number 6299).

Is an Appliance Inside Creating Noise?

Go around the house unplugging, disconnecting, or turning off the breaker to, electronic appliances such as intercoms, baby monitors, TVs, stereos, amplifiers, low-voltage lighting, computers, printers, copiers, and fax machines. Include all PLC controllers and modules that you are not currently testing. Test the problem PLC equipment again. If the problem has disappeared, re-connect the appliances, one at a time, until you find the offending appliance. If the offending appliance is a PLC controller or module, replace the defective module. Otherwise, use a noise filter or reducer on that appliance (see below).

Why? A defective controller or (less likely) a defective module can "transmit" a PLC signal all the time. This interferes with proper PLC transmission.

Some intercoms, baby-monitors, and remote speaker systems transmit their signals over the powerline with AM signals. These types of systems are becoming less and less popular as the cost of less interference prone systems fall. You cannot use such appliances in the same house as PLC devices. (Note that intercoms may interfere only when the TALK bar is pressed.) FM intercoms are less likely to cause PLC interference. Radio and dedicated wire systems do not cause PLC interference.

Some appliances inadvertently create power line noise. These appliances usually have a "switching" power supply, rather than the transformer type. Such appliances include (but are not limited to) computers, printers, copiers, fax machines, TVs, stereos, amplifiers, and low-voltage lighting with "electronic transformers."

You can silence a noisy appliance in several ways:

- If the appliance plugs-in and is rated at 5 amps or less (600 watts), use a Plug-In Noise Filter (Leviton 6288). This little box simply plugs into the wall, and the offending appliance plugs into a socket in the 6288. This box is good for noisy computers, monitors, TVs, amplifiers, and so on.

 Important note: These filters will blow if you try to pull more than 5 amps through them.

- If the appliance is wired in and is rated at 5 amps or less, use a Wire-In Noise Block (Leviton 6287). This very small box has three wires: HOT, NEUTRAL, and LOAD. The 6287 is wired such that the hot goes through the 6287 and to the appliance. This device is good for noisy, wired-in devices such as low-voltage ceiling lights with electronic transformers.

- If the appliance is over 5 amps or 600 watts, use a Leviton 6289 for 110 volt appliances, and one or two 6289s for 220 volt devices. The 6289 is a cylinder with two wires. For 110 volt devices, attach one 6289 wire to the appliance's LINE wire and the other 6289 wire to the appliance's NEUTRAL wire. For 220 volt devices, you can connect one 6289 between the two LINEs, or better yet, connect one 6289 between each LINE and the NEUTRAL or GROUND. The LINE does not go through the 6289 to the appliance, so there is no current rating on the 6289. But because of this, the 6289 is not as effective in eliminating noise, which is why it's called a noise "reducer" instead of a noise filter. You should place the 6289(s) as close as possible to the source of the noise, either where AC enters the appliance, if convenient, or in the wall-box where the appliance is connected. In severe cases, you can use multiple 6289s wired in parallel to further reduce noise.

Do You Have Noise on Your Power Line?

Turn off all breakers except one that does not power any special lighting or electronic appliances. Plug a known good controller and module into an outlet on that breaker. Try to operate the module. If it works, try the same thing on a breaker on the other "phase." (See Figure 6, page 21.) If either of these tests fail, you probably have noise coming into your house on the power line.

Why? In all my experience, I've seen this happen exactly four times. In two of the cases, the houses had underground service, it had been raining heavily, and the neighborhood transformer was in an underground vault, half full of water. The transformer was merrily bubbling away, and I suspect this was the source of the noise. One of these cases was cured with a whole-house noise block (Leviton 6284 Blocking Coupler). The other case underwent spontaneous remission, coinciding with a visit from the electric utility's truck.

The third case of incoming power line noise was in an industrial three-phase site, my showroom, and was cured by a Leviton 6284 noise block.

The last case was never proven, but I believe it was caused by a neighbor's baby monitor. Very unfriendly folks lived next door to this poor fellow. Just after the neighbors brought a new baby home, one "side" of his home quit working. My investigation showed continuous and steady noise on one of the phases, none on the other. While waiting for installation of a noise block, the noise suddenly disappeared, never to be heard from again.

If you have noise coming into your home, there are several things you can do. See the section "Solving External Noise Problems" on page 61 for further information.

4 Mysterious Turn-Ons

"If the bone of a camel is dipped into the juice of the plant eclipta prostata, and then burnt, and the black pigment produced from its ashes is placed in a box also made of the bone of a camel, and applied together with antimony to the eye lashes with a pencil also made of the bone of a camel, then that pigment is said to be very pure, and wholesome for the eyes, and serves as a means of subjugating others to the person who uses it."

—Vatsyayana, Kama Sutra

Follow these steps if you have one or more PLC modules that have mysterious power symptoms such as turning on seemingly by themselves.

These steps assume that you have a (nearly) properly functioning system as a whole. If you have any problems with modules that do not respond properly to remote commands, take care of those problems first, then come back to this chapter.

User Error?

It may sound silly, but before embarking on a troubleshooting expedition, check with other occupants and their visitors to make sure they aren't leaving the lights on, or inadvertently turning them on because of misuse of the system, such as punching the wrong buttons. If you have a maxi-controller (22 buttons), or an old style mini-controller (10 buttons), remember that any unit button that is pressed will be remembered by the system until a command button is pressed. For instance, if a child presses the "6" button, then, an hour later, an adult turns a light on by pressing "1" and "on", both modules 6 and 1 will turn on!

Is Another House Controlling Yours?

Change the House Code of all modules and controllers to another letter, especially if they are currently set to "A".

Why? Your neighbor may have PLC components and may be unknowingly controlling your equipment. If this is the case, changing to another house code is the solution. Many people leave their equipment set to "A", which greatly increases the risk if you are on "A" also.

PLC signals can travel, via the power lines, to other structures on the same distribution transformer. There are usually three to five houses on each distribution transformer. In apartments and condominiums, each building is usually on a separate transformer (six to ten units). If you live in a detached single-family dwelling with above ground power feeds, you can trace the wires to the nearest pole-mounted transformer and determine who else is in your "electrical neighborhood."

Experience has shown that this is rarely the cause, but since it is the easiest thing to try, I suggest trying it first.

If changing house codes does not solve the problem, proceed to the next step.

Is Local Control Biting You?

If the module that is turning on unexpectedly is an X-10 SR227 LM465, AM466, AM486, or SL575 or a Leviton 6227 or 6376, try disabling local control in one of the following ways:

- If the module is an old (dark brown) lamp or appliance module, replace it with a new one.
- For X-10 AM466, AM486, and LM465 modules, you can disable local control by opening up the module and cutting pin 7 of the integrated circuit inside. (See the section "Disabling Local Control" on page 59 for the complete procedure.)
- Plug a multi-outlet extension cord into the module, and plug the device you want to control, plus a night light, or other small (approximately 7 watt) load into the extension cord.
- Change the module to one that does not have local control. (See Table 2, "PLC Modules," on page 57.)

Why? The local control feature, present on many modules, allows the user to force the module on by turning the load off, then back on. It senses this off/on action by trickling a small current through the device. Some loads, like fluorescent light ballasts, can trip the local control soon after they are turned off. Thus, the light turns off by remote control but pops back on within a few seconds. Sometimes a momentary AC line voltage sag, such as when a pump motor comes on, can trip a module's local control. Old (dark brown) modules seem most susceptible to this. Loads with a mechanical thermostat, such as window air conditioners and portable heaters, can trigger local control and turn on as the temperature rises and falls.

Local control being tripped is the most common cause of devices turning on by themselves, *especially* with old "Little Brown Modules" (LBMs).

If none of the above fix the problem, proceed to the next step.

Is a Timer Doing More Than it's Supposed To?

Make sure that it's not a timer that is turning the device on by unplugging the timer(s) and seeing if the problem reoccurs.

Timers include X-10 part numbers MT522 and CP290, Leviton part numbers 6311 and 6312, other whole-house controllers, and computer interfaces.

Why? It's very rare, but a defective timer can send a command when it isn't supposed to. More often, the timer is programmed incorrectly. Remember that the MT522 and 6312 timers allow *two* on and off settings per device! With the CP290, other whole-house controllers, and computer interfaces, it's pretty easy to set up, and then forget about, a timed event.

If the device comes on at around the same time each day or week, and you have a timer in your system, a defective timer is the most likely cause.

If the "unplug" test identifies a timer as the culprit, reprogram or replace the timer. Otherwise go to the next step.

Are They "Held Off" Commands?

If you have any Leviton 6319 or 6400 series wall-mount controllers in your system, test all controllers (not just the wall-mount ones) for proper operation and replace any defective ones. Then disconnect each controller long enough to determine if the problem goes away.

Alternatively, use a noise meter to determine if any controller is constantly transmitting (hunt down and replace any such controller) or if there is any other source of noise. Also try to notice if the module(s) turn on when you turn *off* any other equipment, regardless of whether it is PLC controlled. If so, isolate the equipment you turned off. See the section "PLC Signal Transmission Problems" on page 11.

Why? The Leviton 6319 and 6400 series wall-mount controllers have feature called "hold-off." While it is a great feature, it can create some misleading symptoms if there are other problems with your system. The hold-off feature causes these controllers to wait for a "clear" line before sending commands. The controllers store commands indefinitely, so button presses made last week are suddenly transmitted when a noisy, high-intensity light is finally turned off.

If you've gotten this far, and you have Leviton 6319 or 6400 series controllers, I would strongly suspect that either one of your controllers is "stuck" on (transmitting all the time), or you have a serious noise problem. It's rare, but I have seen virtually every kind of controller malfunction and transmit all the time. Other than by trial and error, you will need a noise meter to track down the stuck controller or the source of the line noise.

Is Random Line Noise Turning it On?

Use the Signal Strength Indicator (page 69) to check for line noise.

See the section "Is an Appliance Inside Creating Noise?" on page 22 for a guide on finding and isolating line noise. Remember that line noise may only be present at certain times of the day, when certain equipment is on. It may be fleeting. (But then it would be even less likely to be the cause.) Turn on everything in the house before checking for noise, especially computers, printers, all low-voltage lights, fluorescent lights, and lights on dimmers. If you find noise, snuff it out at its source, or block it from entering your house if it is coming in on your main feed. For more information, see the section "Do You Have Noise on Your Power Line?" on page 23.

Why? A module will turn on when it receives a specific digitally coded message. Random line noise is unlikely to exactly reproduce this message by accident. But if the level noise is consistently high, and it goes on for days and weeks, probability goes right out the window. Like the man trying to open a lock with an infinite number of random keys at his disposal, sooner or later one of those keys may indeed work! Another factor is whether or not the module in question responds to the "all lights on" command. Modules that do not (see Table 2 on page 57) are far less likely to be falsely triggered by noise. Where the module that responds to "all lights on" turns on when it receives this single command, modules that do not must receive two commands, in the proper order. (The module select code, and the on command.) The odds are simply astronomical.

If the module that is turning itself on responds to "all lights on," and you have constant noise, this may well be the problem. (But the rest of your system probably isn't working at all well either.) If the module does not respond to "all lights on," or you do not have a serious noise problem, go on to the next step.

What Else Could it Be?

If you've gotten this far without a solution, it's probably because you are having difficulty reproducing the problem. Perhaps it happens so rarely that it's difficult to tell when you really *have* solved the problem. If so, think about when the problem has occurred in the past. Was it unusually hot or cold? (Temperature related?) Had it just rained a lot? (Moisture getting into something or lightning causing power problems?) Was it very windy? (Power fluctuations?) You may have to wait for Mother Nature, or your "electrical neighbors," to reproduce the environment of the failure before it will occur again.

If the problem suddenly appeared in an existing installation, identify new lights and appliances that have been added to the household. Be particularly suspicious of these new devices. See if you can "link" the problem with when these new devices are used.

You could replace the module that is turning on by itself. But other than through local control, I've never seen a module fail in this manner.

5 Three- and Four-Way Switch Wiring

"Could you expect me to rejoice in the inferiority of your connections?"

—Jane Austen, *Pride and Prejudice*

One the most common calls I received is about three- and four-way switch wiring. Rather than jump right in with troubleshooting multiway switch installations, this chapter first demystifies these disconcerting beasts by explaining terminology and common wiring practices. Since most multiway switch installation problems are related to miswiring the wall-switch modules, we present step-by-step installation instructions.

Terminology

A three-way switch has *two* switches that operate the device, a four-way switch has *three or more* switches. The terminology comes from the number of terminals on the switches, not the number of switches.

Three kinds of wires connect to three- and four-way switches:

Line (also called hot or live). This black wire carries un-switched AC (measured against neutral or ground). This wire connects to only one switch, and never directly to the load.

Traveler. There are at least two traveler wires in any three- or four-way switch setup. Travelers may be any color, including red. Travelers always connect only between switches, never directly to the load. Depending on the current switch positions, a traveler wire may be in any one of three states: It may be hot, carrying 120 volts AC (even if the load is "off"); **floating** (unconnected at either end); low (connected to the load on one end but unconnected at the other end.)

Switched-Line. This wire is also called load, switched-live, or switched-hot. It carries 120 volts AC to the load when the switches are in an "on" configuration. In a standard lamp socket, this is a black wire that is connected to the center terminal (the bulb's "base".) This wire always connects to a switch on one end, and the load on the other.

Determining What Each Wire Is

The hardest part of wiring three- and four-way switches is figuring out which wire is which. A voltmeter is helpful, but wires may show an AC voltage even when unconnected. (They may run beside powered wires, "coupling" some voltage to the disconnected wire.) A wire measuring anything less than full and unwavering line voltage is *not* a LINE. A simple neon AC tester is less likely to be fooled by this false voltage as it places a larger load on the wire. You can use a voltmeter or a neon AC tester to identify a LINE, but you will have to identify all other wires through the process of elimination.

The circuit tester, described on page 70, has the additional ability to identify a switched-line by detecting its connection, through a load, to neutral. A wire not identified as a line or switched-line is a traveler.

Typical Three-Way Wiring

Figure shows three common methods of wiring three-way switches. All three circuits are electrically identical, but the wires that enter individual boxes are different.

Three-way circuits always have two, three-terminal switches. The one terminal that is a different color is the common terminal (marked "C" in the figures).

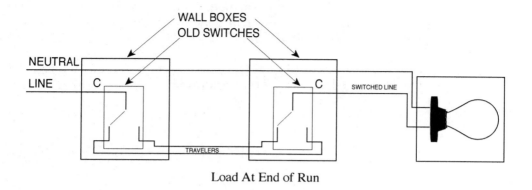

Load At End of Run

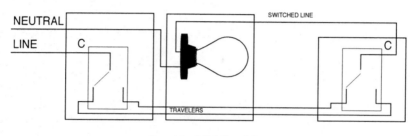

Load In Middle of Run

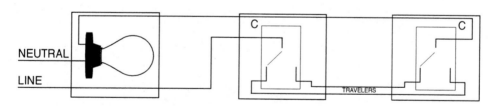

Load At Beginning of Run

Figure 7. Three common methods of wiring three way switches

Typical Four-Way Wiring

Figure 8 shows a common wiring method of a four-way circuit.

Four-way circuits always have two, three-terminal switches at each end of the run, and one or more four-terminal switches in the middle of the run.

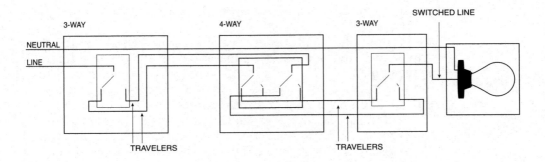

Figure 8. Four-Way Switch Wiring

Installing an X-10 Three-Way Switch

The X-10 three-way switch set, part number WS477, includes the switching module (part number WS477) and a companion switch (part number CS277). Both have three connections, as do the mechanical switches they replace. The module and companion switch can go in either switch location. The instructions that accompany the switches adequately describe the installation, providing you have not yet removed the mechanical switches. If you've removed the mechanical switches, you can no longer look at the screw terminal colors to tell which terminal is the common.

The following two procedures describe how to hook up the three-way wall switch set assuming the worst case: You have three unlabeled and disconnected wires hanging out of each wall-box. You will need a voltmeter, AC voltage tester, or circuit tester as described on page 70. The load (fixture, bulb, etc.) must be connected and, if there is a local switch, turned on. You can install the WS477 and CS277 in either wall box. The first set of instructions should be used if you are connecting the companion switch (X-10 part CS277) between the switching module (X-10 WS477) and the load. The second set of instructions should be used if you are connecting the switching module between the companion switch and the load (see Figure 9).

Connecting the companion switch between the switching module and the load

1. **Make sure that no wires are touching anything. Turn on the breaker.**

2. **One of the six wires from the wall boxes has full line voltage. Locate this wire with your test equipment and label it LINE. If you have a circuit tester, locate the wire in the other box that indicates neutral and label it LOAD.**

If you do not have a circuit tester, in the box with the LINE wire, note the colors and any other identifying characteristics of the other two wires (the travelers). At the other box, label the other end of these same two wires. Label the *remaining* wire LOAD. You must identify one LINE wire in one box, and one LOAD wire in the other box.

3. **Turn off the breaker. Connect the blue WS477 wire to the wire you labeled LINE.**

4. Connect the red WS477 switch wire to one of the two remaining wires from the box. In the box at left, mark the color of the wire from the box you just connected to the red wire.

5. Connect the black WS477 wire to the remaining wire from the box.

6. At the other box, connect one of the blue CS277 wires to the wire you labeled LOAD.

7. Connect the red CS277 wire to the remaining wire of the color you noted in step 4.

8. Connect the remaining blue CS277 wire to the remaining wire.

9. Mount the switches, set the house and unit code dials, turn on the power, and test.

Connecting the switching module between the companion switch and the load

1. Make sure that no wires are touching anything. Turn on the breaker.

2. One of the six wires from the wall boxes has full line voltage. Locate this wire with your test equipment and label it LINE. If you have a circuit tester, locate the wire in the other box that indicates neutral and label it LOAD.

If you do not have a circuit tester, in the box with the LINE wire, note the colors and any other identifying characteristics of the other two wires (the travelers.) At the other box, label the other end of these same two wires. Label the *remaining* wire LOAD. You must identify one LINE wire in one box, and one LOAD wire in the other box.

3. Turn off the breaker. Connect either blue CS277 wire to the wire you labeled LINE.

4. Connect the red CS277 switch wire to one of the two remaining wires from the box. In the box at left, mark the color of the wire from the box you just connected to the red wire.

5. Connect the blue CS277 wire to the remaining wire from the box.

6. At the other box, connect the blue WS477 wire to the wire you labeled LOAD.

7. **Connect the red WS477 wire to the remaining wire of the color you noted in step 4.**

8. **Connect the black WS477 wire to the remaining wire.**

9. **Mount the switches, set the house and unit code dials, turn on the power, and test.**

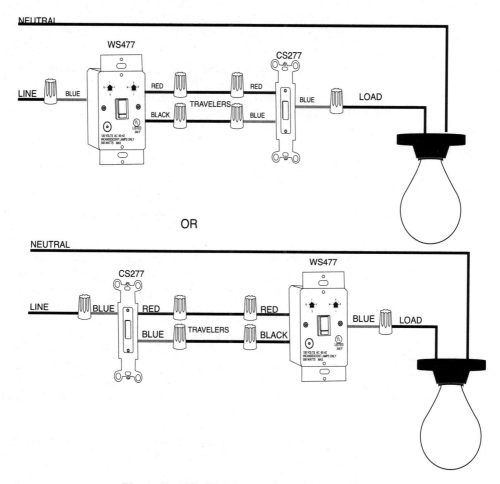

Figure 9. WS477 3-Way Switch Wiring

Installing a 6383 Incandescent Three-Way Switch

The Leviton three-way switch set consists of a three-way switch module (6383-WI) and a slave switch (6294-W or 6294-I). The switch module has three connections, the slave switch has two. The switch module may go in either the line or the load box (see Figure 10).

The following procedure describes how to hook up the three-way wall switch set assuming the worst case: You have three unlabeled and disconnected wires hanging out of each wall-box. You will need a voltmeter, AC tester, or circuit tester as described on page 70. The load (fixture, bulb, etc.) must be connected and, if there is a local switch, turned on.

1. **Make sure that no wires are touching anything. Turn on the breaker.**

One of the six wires from the wall boxes has full line voltage.

2. **Locate this wire with your test equipment and label it LINE. If you have a circuit tester, locate the neutral wire in the other box using your test equipment and label it LOAD.**

If you do not have a circuit tester, in the box with the LINE wire, note the colors and any other identifying characteristics of the other two wires (the travelers). At the other box, label the other end of these same two wires. Label the *remaining* wire LOAD. You must identify one LINE wire in one box, and one LOAD wire in the other box.

3. **Turn off the breaker. Connect the blue 6383 wire to the wire you labeled LOAD.**

4. **Connect the red 6383 wire to one of the two remaining wires from the box.**

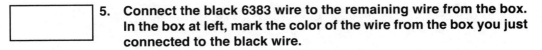

5. **Connect the black 6383 wire to the remaining wire from the box. In the box at left, mark the color of the wire from the box you just connected to the black wire.**

6. **At the other box, connect the wire you labeled LINE and the other wire of the color you noted in step five to one terminal of the 6294.**

You may connect a short (3 inch) jumper wire to the screw terminal, then use a wire-nut to connect this wire to the other two.

7. **Connect the remaining wire from the box to the remaining 6294 screw terminal.**

8. **Mount the switches, set the house and unit code dials, turn on the power, and test.**

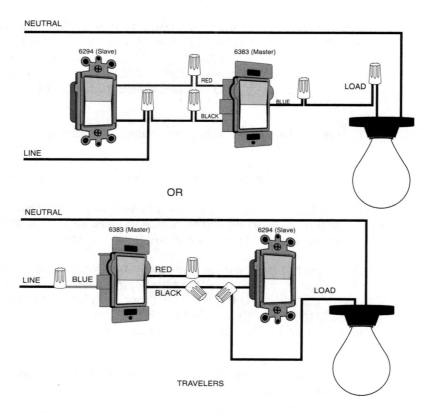

Figure 10. 6383 Incandescent 3-Way Switch Wiring

Installing a 6383-U Universal Three-Way Switch

The Leviton universal three-way switch set consists of a universal three-way switch module (6383-UWI) and a slave switch (6294-W or 6294-I). The universal switch module has four connections, the slave switch has two. The switch module must go in the box with the LOAD wire (see Figure 11).

The following procedure describes how to hook up the three-way wall switch set assuming the worst case: You have three unlabeled and disconnected wires hanging out of each wall-box. You will need a voltmeter, AC tester, or circuit tester as described on page 70. The load (fixture, bulb, etc.) must be connected and, if there is a local switch, turned on.

1. **Make sure that no wires are touching anything. Turn on the breaker.**

One of the six wires from the wall boxes has full line voltage.

2. **Locate this wire with your test equipment and label it LINE. If you have a circuit tester, locate the wire in the other box that indicates neutral and label it LOAD.**

If you do not have a circuit tester, in the box with the LINE wire, note the colors and any other identifying characteristics of the other two wires (the travelers.) At the other box, label the other end of these same two wires. Label the *remaining* wire LOAD. You must identify one LINE wire in one box, and one LOAD wire in the other box.

3. **Turn off the breaker. Connect the blue 6383-U wire to the wire you labeled LOAD.**

4. **Connect the red 6383-U wire to one of the two remaining wires from the box.**

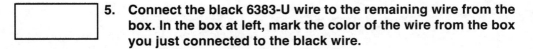

5. **Connect the black 6383-U wire to the remaining wire from the box. In the box at left, mark the color of the wire from the box you just connected to the black wire.**

6. **Connect the white 6383-U wire to a neutral in the box.**

A neutral is a white wire that does not connect to any switch in the box.

7. **At the other box, connect the wire you labeled LINE and the wire of the color you noted in step five to one terminal of the 6294.**

You may connect a short (3 inch) jumper wire to the screw terminal, then use a wire-nut to connect this wire to the other two.

8. **Connect the remaining wire from the box to the remaining 6294 screw terminal.**

9. **Mount the switches, set the house and unit code dials, turn on the power, and test.**

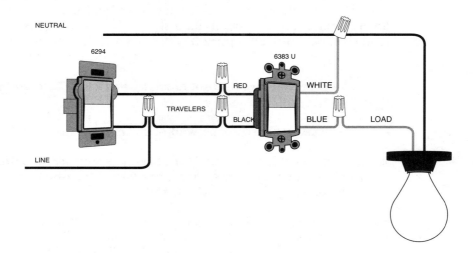

Figure 11. 6383-U 3-Way Switch Wiring

Installing a 6293 Three-Way Relay Switch

The Leviton three-way relay switch set consists of a three-way relay switch module (6293-WI) and a slave switch (6294-W or 6294-I). The switch module has four connections, the slave switch has two. The switch module must go in the box with the LOAD wire (see Figure 12).

The following procedure describes how to hook up the three-way wall switch set assuming the worst case: You have three unlabeled and disconnected wires hanging out of each wall-box. You will need a voltmeter, AC tester, or circuit tester as described on page 70. The load (fixture, bulb, etc.) must be connected and, if there is a local switch, turned on.

1. **Make sure that no wires are touching anything. Turn on the breaker.**

One of the six wires from the wall boxes has full line voltage.

2. **Locate this wire with your test equipment and label it LINE. If you have a circuit tester, locate the wire in the other box that indicates neutral and label it LOAD.**

If you do not have a circuit tester, in the box with the LINE wire, note the colors and any other identifying characteristics of the other two wires (the travelers.) At the other box, label the other end of these same two wires. Label the *remaining* wire LOAD. You must identify one LINE wire in one box, and one LOAD wire in the other box.

3. **Turn off the breaker. Connect the wire you labeled LOAD to the LOAD terminal on the 6293.**

4. **Connect one of the two remaining wires from the box to the CONTROL terminal on the 6293.**

5. **Connect the remaining wire from the box to the LINE terminal on the 6293. In the box at left, mark the color of the wire.**

6. **Connect a neutral in the box to the NEUTRAL terminal on the 6293.**

A neutral is a white wire that does not connect to any switch in the box.

7. **At the other box, connect the wire you labeled LINE and the wire of the color you noted in step five to one terminal of the 6294.**

You may connect a short (3 inch) jumper wire to the screw terminal, then use a wire-nut to connect this wire to the other two.

8. **Connect the remaining wire from the box to the remaining 6294 screw terminal.**

9. **Mount the switches, set the house and unit code dials, turn on the power, and test.**

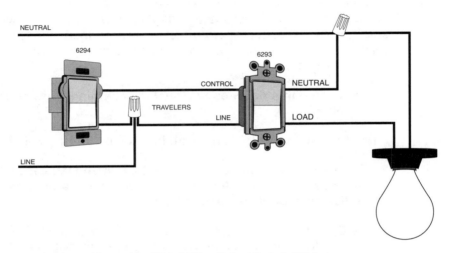

Figure 12. 6293 3-Way Relay Switch Wiring

Installing an X-10 Four-Way Switch

A four-way switch can be achieved with X-10 by using the WS4777 set and adding one CS277 companion switch for each extra switch position. The module and one companion switch can go in either end location, but to simplify things, I'll describe the installation where the WS477 goes in the LINE box (see Figure 13).

The following procedure describes how to hook up the four-way wall switch set assuming the worst case: You have three or four unlabeled and disconnected wires hanging out of each wall-box. You should have three unconnected wires in two boxes, these are the *end* boxes. You should have four unconnected wires in the other boxes, these are the *middle* boxes. You will need a voltmeter, AC tester, or circuit tester as described on page 70. The load (fixture, bulb, etc.) must be connected and, if there is a local switch, turned on.

1. **Make sure that no wires are touching anything. Turn on the breaker.**

One of the wires in the three-wire boxes has full line voltage.

2. **Locate this wire with your test equipment and label it LINE. If you have a circuit tester, locate the wire in the other three-wire box that indicates neutral and label it LOAD.**

If you do not have a circuit tester, you must determine which two wires in the non-LINE three-wire box are the travelers and label them. Label the *remaining* wire LOAD. You must identify one LINE wire in one three-wire box, and one LOAD wire in the other three-wire box.

Line End Box

3. **Turn off the breaker. Connect the blue WS477 wire to the wire you labeled LINE.**

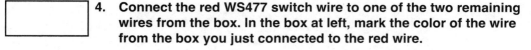

4. **Connect the red WS477 switch wire to one of the two remaining wires from the box. In the box at left, mark the color of the wire from the box you just connected to the red wire.**

5. **Connect the black WS477 wire to the remaining wire from the box.**

Load End Box

6. At the other end box, connect one of the blue CS277 wires to the wire you labeled LOAD.

7. Connect the red CS277 wire to the remaining wire of the color you noted in step 4.

8. Connect the remaining blue CS277 wire to the remaining wire.

Middle (4-Way) Boxes

9. Connect the red CS277 wire to *both* wires of the color you noted in step 4.

10. Connect one blue CS277 wire to each of the remaining wires. Repeat steps 9 and 10 for each remaining middle box.

11. Mount the switches, set the house and unit code dials, turn on the power, and test.

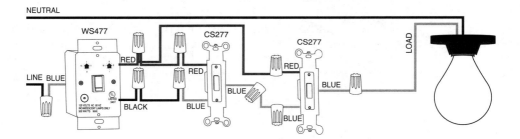

Figure 13. WS477 4-Way Switch Wiring

Installing a 6383 Incandescent Four-Way Switch

An incandescent four-way switch can be achieved with a 6383-WI and one 6294 slave switch for each additional switch position. The 6383-WI module can go in either end location. But to simplify things, I'll describe the installation where the 6383-WI goes in the LOAD box (see Figure 14).

The following procedure describes how to hook up the four-way wall switch set assuming the worst case: You have three or four unlabeled and disconnected wires hanging out of each wall-box. You should have three unconnected wires in two boxes, which are the *end* boxes. You should have four unconnected wires in the other boxes, which are the *middle* boxes. You will need a voltmeter, AC tester, or circuit tester as described on page 70. The load (fixture, bulb, etc.) must be connected and, if there is a local switch, turned on.

1. **Make sure that no wires are touching anything. Turn on the breaker.**

One of the wires in the three-wire boxes has full line voltage.

2. **Locate this wire with your test equipment and label it LINE. If you have a circuit tester, locate the wire in the other three-wire box that indicates neutral and label it LOAD.**

If you do not have a circuit tester, you must determine which two wires in the non-LINE three-wire box are the travelers and label them. Label the *remaining* wire LOAD. You must identify one LINE wire in one three-wire box, and one LOAD wire in the other three-wire box.

Load End Box

3. **Turn off the breaker. Connect the blue 6383 wire to the wire you labeled LOAD in step 2.**

4. **Connect the red 6383 wire to one of the two remaining wires from the box. In the box at left, mark the color of the wire from the box you just connected to the red wire.**

5. **Connect the black 6383 wire to the remaining wire from the box. In the box at left, mark the color of the wire from the box you just connected to the black wire.**

Line End Box

6. At the other end box, connect the wire you labeled LINE, and the wire from the box of the color you noted in step 5 to one screw terminal. (You may need to use a stub and wire-nut.)

7. Connect the wire of the color you noted in step 4 to the other screw terminal.

Middle (Four-Way) Boxes

8. Connect *both* wires of the color you noted in step 4 to one screw terminal.

9. Connect *both* wires of the color you noted in step 5 to the remaining screw terminal.
    Repeat steps 8 and 9 for each remaining middle box.

10. Mount the switches, set the house and unit code dials, turn on the power, and test.

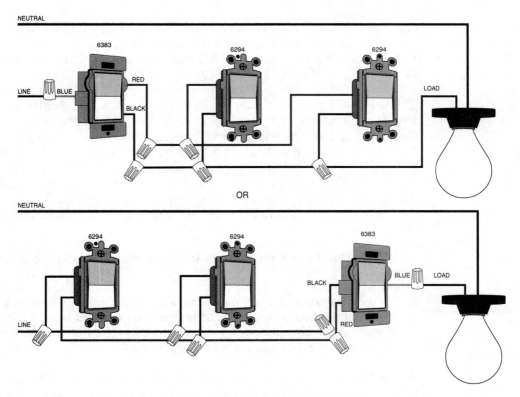

Figure 14. 6383 Incandescent 4-Way Switch Wiring

Installing a 6383-U Universal Four-Way Switch

A universal four-way switch can be achieved with a 6383-UWI and one 6294 slave switch for each additional switch position. The 6383-UWI module must go in the LOAD box. There must also be a neutral in this box (see Figure 15).

The following procedure describes how to hook up the four-way wall switch set assuming the worst case: You have three or four unlabeled and disconnected wires hanging out of each wall-box. You should have three unconnected wires in two boxes, which are the *end* boxes. You should have four unconnected wires in the other boxes, which are the *middle* boxes. You will need a voltmeter, AC tester, or circuit tester as described on page 70. The load (fixture, bulb, etc.) must be connected and, if there is a local switch, turned on.

1. **Make sure that no wires are touching anything. Turn on the breaker.**

2. **One of the wires in the three-wire boxes will have full line voltage. Locate this wire with your test equipment and label it LINE. If you have a circuit tester, locate the wire in the other three-wire box that indicates neutral and label it LOAD.**

If you do not have a circuit tester, you must determine which two wires in the non-LINE three-wire box are the travelers and label them. Label the *remaining* wire LOAD. You must identify one LINE wire in one three-wire box, and one LOAD wire in the other three-wire box.

Load End Box

3. **Turn off the breaker. Connect the blue 6383-U wire to the wire you labeled LOAD.**

4. **Connect the red 6383-U wire to one of the two remaining wires from the end box. In the box at left, mark the color of the wire from the box you just connected to the red wire.**

5. **Connect the black 6383-U wire to the remaining wire from the end box. Mark the color of the wire from the box you just connected to the black wire in the box.**

6. **Connect the white 6383-U wire to a neutral in the box.**

Line End Box

7. At the other end box, connect the wire you labeled LINE, and the wire from the box of the color you noted in step 5 to one screw terminal. (You may need to use a stub and wire-nut.)

8. Connect the wire of the color you noted in step 4 to the other screw terminal.

Middle (Four-Way) Boxes

9. Connect *both* wires of the color you noted in step 4 to one screw terminal.

10. Connect *both* wires of the color you noted in step 5 to the remaining screw terminal.
    Repeat steps 9 and 10 for each remaining middle box.

11. Mount the switches, set the house and unit code dials, turn on the power, and test.

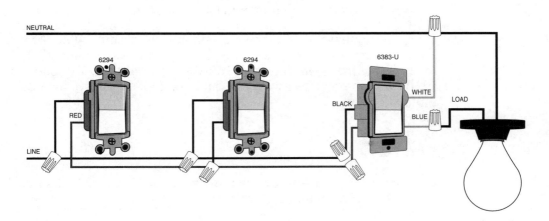

Figure 15. 6383 Incandescent 4-Way Switch Wiring

Installing a 6293 Four-Way Relay Switch

A four-way relay switch can be achieved with a 6293-WI and one 6294 slave switch for each additional switch position. The 6293-UWI module must go in the LOAD box. There must also be a neutral in this box (see Figure 16).

The following procedure describes how to hook up the four-way wall switch set assuming the worst case: You have three or four unlabeled and disconnected wires hanging out of each wall-box. You should have three unconnected wires in two boxes, which are the *end* boxes. You should have four unconnected wires in the other boxes, which are the *middle* boxes. You will need a voltmeter, AC tester, or circuit tester as described on page 70. The load (fixture, bulb, etc.) must be connected and, if there is a local switch, turned on.

1. **Make sure that no wires are touching anything. Turn on the breaker.**

2. **One of the wires in the three-wire boxes has full line voltage. Locate this wire with your test equipment and label it LINE. If you have a circuit tester, locate the wire in the other three-wire box that indicates neutral and label it LOAD.**

If you do not have a circuit tester, you must determine which two wires in the non-LINE three-wire box are the travelers and label them. Label the *remaining* wire LOAD. You must identify one LINE wire in one three-wire box, and one LOAD wire in the other three-wire box.

Load End Box

3. **Turn off the breaker. Connect the wire you labeled LOAD to the LOAD screw terminal of the 6293.**

4. **Connect one of the two remaining wires from the end box to the CONTROL screw terminal. In the box at left, mark the color of the wire you just connected.**

5. **Connect the remaining wire from the end box to the LINE screw terminal. In the box at left, mark the color of the wire you just connected.**

6. **Connect the NEUTRAL screw terminal to a neutral wire in the box.**

Line End Box

7. At the other end box, connect the wire you labeled LINE, and the wire from the box of the color you noted in step 5 to one screw terminal. (You may need to use a stub and wire-nut.)

8. Connect the wire of the color you noted in step 4 to the other screw terminal.

Middle (Four-Way) Boxes

9. Connect *both* wires of the color you noted in step 4 to one screw terminal.

10. Connect *both* wires of the color you noted in step 5 to the remaining screw terminal.

11. Repeat steps 9 and 10 for each remaining middle box.

12. Mount the switches, set the house and unit code dials, turn on the power, and test.

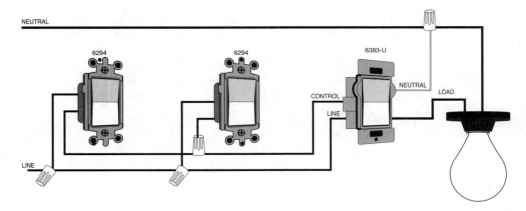

Figure 16. 6293 4-Way Relay Switch Wiring

Wired Hot Fixtures

Occasionally, a switch and load is wired incorrectly in the first place. The most common, and dangerous, is the "wired hot" fixture. This is where the line is connected to the load, and the other side of the load is brought to the switches. This **post load line** is then switched to the neutral. If this is the case, no amount of juggling the switch wires can allow the use of X-10 or Leviton products. If you encounter this problem, rewire the fixture correctly before trying to automate it.

6 Module And Controller Specifications

"If you work with glue, sooner or later you're bound to get stuck."

—Leo Tolstoy, *War and Peace*

The tables on the next several pages will help you find the proper module for a given load and find a controller that will do what you want.

The formulas in this chapter can assist you in determining the load rating required for a particular application.

Incandescent Lamp Ratings

Standard incandescent light bulbs are rated in **watts.** You can convert a wattage rating to amps by dividing by 120 (volts).

```
amps = watts/volts
```

Conversely, you can convert amps to watts by multiplying by 120 volts.

```
watts = amps * 120
```

But the one thing this calculation doesn't take into account is **inrush**. When an incandescent bulb is first turned on, its resistance is much lower than after it has run for a while. Very briefly, the lamp pulls much more current (up to 10 times more) than normal. This "inrush" is not counted in the wattage of the bulb. If a module's ampere rating includes the word "incandescent," then the manufacturer has already accounted for the inrush. So, when converting watts to amps, multiply by an extra 3.6. And when converting from amps to watts, divide the amps by 3.6 before multiplying by the voltage. Exceeding the resulting recommended ratings may seem to work, but you will probably shorten the life of the module.

Here are simplified formulas for finding incandescent lamp ratings, assuming 120 volt lighting:

```
Incandescent Watts x 0.03 = Required Amp Rating

Amp Rating/ 0.03 = Maximum Incandescent Rating
```

 Note that the formulas above use the number "0.03" to convert from watts to amps and amps to watts. This number is derived by taking the multiplication factor, 3.6, and dividing by standard line voltage, 120.

120 Volt Quartz Lamp Ratings

Quartz lamps have a much lower inrush than standard (tungsten) incandescent lamps. I use a 1.8 multiplier to account for quartz lamp inrush. The simplified formulas are:

```
Quartz Watts x .015 = Required Amp Rating

Amp Rating/.015 = Maximum Quartz Rating
```

Local Control

If a module has the "Local Control" column marked, the module can be "forced" on by turning the attached appliance off, then back on.

Requires Neutral

Most modules require a neutral wire connection for proper operation. A few replacement wall switches for incandescent lights do not require a neutral. This simplifies wiring.

Tables

In the tables that follow, the color codes are "B" for beige, "W" for white, and "I" for Ivory. A "•" signifies that the module or controller has a specific feature; a blank box signifies that the module or controller does not have that feature.

Table 2: PLC Modules

Type	Model	Color	3-way	Local Control	Indicator Light	Requires Neutral	AllOn	Dim	Incandescent	120V Quartz	Fluorescent Low voltage and Motors	Requires
Wall switch	6291-WI	WI			•	•	•		2400W		20A	Coverplate
	6293-WI	WI	•		•	•	•		2400W		20A	Coverplate, 6294
	6294-	B,W,I	Slave									6293 or 6383
	6381-WI	WI					•	•	60-500W*		No	Coverplate
	6383-WI	WI	•				•	•	60-500W*		No	Coverplate, 6294
	6381-UWI	WI				•	•	•	60-500W*		500VA	Coverplate
	6383-UWI	WI	•			•	•	•	60-500W*		500VA	Coverplate, 6294
	6371-I	I			•	•	•		1300W	2600W	20A 250V	Coverplate
	WS467	I					•	•	60-500W*		No	
	WS4777	I	•				•	•	60-500W*		No	
	CS277	I	Slave									WS4777
Wall outlet	6227-?	B,W,I		•		•			500W	1000W	15A	
	6280-?	B,W,I				•			500W	1000W	15A	
	6296-?	B,W,I				•			650W	1300W	20A	
	6297-I	I				•			1000W	2000W	15A 250V	
	6298-?	B,W,I				•			1300W	2600W	20A 250V	
	SR227	I		•		•			500W	1000W	15A	
Wire-in	6290					•	•	•	2400W		2400VA	
	6375					•	•		2400W		20A	
	6376			•		•	•	•	300W		No	
Plug-in	HD243	I				•			1000W	2000W	15A 250V	
	HD245	I				•			1300W	2600W	20A 250V	
	LM465	I		•		•	•	•	300W		No	
	AM466	I		•		•			500W	1000W	15A (1/3HP)	
	AM486	I		•		•			500W	1000W	15A (1/3HP)	
	UM506	I			Beep	•			No		100VA 30V	Low-voltage wire
	SC546	I			Chime	•			No			
Screw-in	SL575	W		•		•	•	•	300W		No	

* Reduce the maximum rating by 100w for each switch when two or more are together in a wall box. For example, the maximum load for two switches is 400w, for three switches, it's 300w.

Table 3: PLC Controllers

Description	Model	Color	Number of Addresses	Sends Commands		Command Source	Requires
				AllOn/ AllOff	Bright/ Dim		
Mini-controller	MC460		4	•	•	User keypress	
Maxi-controller	SC503		16	•	•	User lepers	
Controller body	6400		4	•	•	Keypad	6450 Keypad
Wall-mount keypad	6450-4	I,W	4			User keypress	6400 Controller body
	6450-4D	I,W	3		•		
	6450-4A	I,W	3	•			
	6450-2	I,W	2				
	6450-2D	I,W	1		•		
	6450-1	I,W	1				
	6450-1A	I,W	0	•			
Dry-contact transmitter	6315		4			Four contacts On=open Off=closed	
	6316		4			Four contacts On/Off when closed	
Interflash controller	6326		1	•		6 to 24 volt input	
Powerflash interface	PF284		1	•		Contact closure or 6-18VAC/ DC	Signal source (reed switch, etc.), wire
Motion-detector/light	PR511		8			Motion detection, ambient light, delay	Bulbs
Sundowner	SD533		4	•	•	User keypress, ambient light	
Photocell	6308		4			Ambient light, delay	
Telephone responder	TR551		10			Touch tones	
Plug-in transceivers	TM751		16		•	UHF from 6313, RT504, RW684, RW694, RW724, or KC674	UHF transmitter
	RR501		8		•		
UHF Remote	RT504		8/16		•	User keypress	RR501 or TM751; 4 AAA batteries.
Wireless keyfob	KC674		2				RR501 or TM751; 2 AAA batteries
Wireless wall-switches	RW684		2				RR501 or TM751; 4 AAA batteries
	RW694		4				
	RW724		3		•		
Deluxe wall mount timer	6311-	I,W	256	•	•	63 User programs	4 AA batteries
Basic wall mount timer	6312-	I,W	4	•	•	16 User programs	4 AAA batteries
Mini-timer	MT522		4/8	•	•	16 user programs	9v battery

7 Miscellaneous Procedures

"In Naples they caponize two or three thousand boys every year; some die of it, others acquire a voice more beautiful than a woman's, others go and govern states."

—Voltaire, *Candide*

This chapter collects a variety of procedures that you may find useful in troubleshooting your home automation system.

Disabling Local Control

The local control feature, present on many modules, allows the user to force the module on by turning the load off, then back on. It senses this off/on action by trickling a small current through the device. Some loads, like fluorescent light ballasts, can trip the local control soon after they are turned off. Thus the light turns off by remote control, but pops back on within a few seconds. Sometimes a momentary AC line voltage sag (such as when a motor turns on) can trip a module's local control. Old (dark brown) modules seem most susceptible to this. Loads with a mechanical thermostat, such as window air conditioners and portable heaters, can trigger local control and turn on as the temperature rises and falls.

You can disable local control in several ways ("Is Local Control Biting You?" on page 26). For X-10 part numbers AM466, AM486, and LM465 modules, you can disable local control inside the module with the following procedure.

The Local Control feature is driven by pin number 7 of the custom integrated circuit (IC) found in the modules listed above; therefore, to disable local control, you need to disconnect pin number 7.

1. **Use a long, thin screwdriver to remove the screw between the two flat prongs of the plug. Carefully pry off the front part of the case. Don't lose the house and unit code dials when they fall out. Remove the internal circuitry from the back half of the case.**

2. **Compare the component side of the circuit board with Figure 17. Locate the custom integrated circuit noted in Figure 17.**

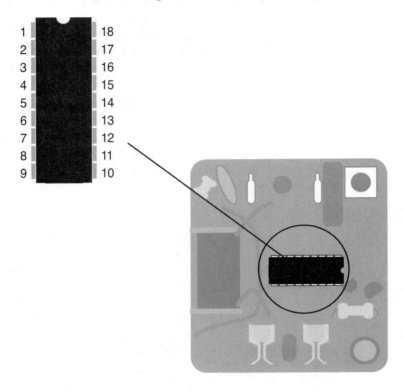

Figure 17. Disabling Local Control—IC Location

3. **Locate pin number 7 by counting counter-clockwise starting at the notch in the integrated circuit.**

4. **Once you've located pin number 7, disable it in one of three ways:**

   - **Cut the pin itself.**
   - **Cut the trace that the pin is connected to on the reverse side of the circuit board.**
   - **Cut the jumper soldered to the end of the trace.**

Only choose to cut the pin itself if you have the proper tools. Otherwise, use a hobby knife or other sharp instrument to cut the trace, or turn the circuit board over, identify the jumper attached to the trace, and use a small wire cutter to carefully cut it and separate the ends.

Solving External Noise Problems

The most distressing problem to have when trying to get PLC equipment to work is external noise. This is where powerline noise comes in through your electrical service and disrupts the transmission of PLC signals. While it may sound disastrous and unsolvable, there are several steps you can take to solve this problem.

Is it Really External Noise?

First, make sure it really is an external noise problem (see the section "Do You Have Noise on Your Power Line?" on page 23). If possible, verify the presence of outside noise with a Signal Strength Indicator and an Automatic Test Transmitter, connected directly to each phase in turn, with all breakers off. If the ERROR light comes on, you do have external noise. Note which phases have noise. It is important to verify the presence of external noise before going on; otherwise, you'll be wasting your time.

Learn More About the Noise

Next, you can learn more about the nature of the external noise. Most powerline noise doesn't interfere with PLC transmissions. The noise has to be at or around 120Khz (or contain some component at 120Khz), the noise has to occur at sufficient amplitude to interfere (at or above 20mV), and it must occur at the right point in the powerline cycle (zero crossing). If the Signal Strength Indicator's ERROR light comes on, noise meeting all these factors is present. But we can go further, finding out if the noise is always present, and if the noise varies in intensity.

You can make a Line Noise Monitor (Figure 18). This device allows you to see the noise on a digital voltmeter (DVM). The signal bridge filters out the 120Khz signal from the powerline. Normally, the other side of the bridge is connected to the other phase, where it imposes the signal onto that phase. In this use, we're just looking at the low-voltage AC signal coming out of the bridge.

Line Noise Monitor

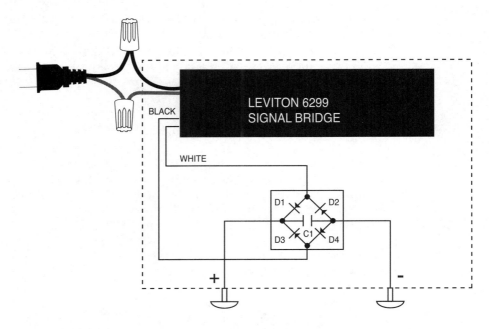

Parts List

1   Signal Bridge
1   AC Plug & Line Cord (Cut up extension cord)
4   D1-D4 Diodes 1N4001 or equivalent
1   C1 Capacitor.2Mfd approx. (RS 272-1 35 x 2 wire in parallel)
2   Binding Posts (RS 274-0662)
1   Small Perfboard (RS 276-1395)
1   Case (RS 270-627)

Figure 18. Line Noise Monitor

The diodes D1 through D4 are arranged in a bridge, they convert the low-voltage AC signal to low-voltage DC. C1 is added to average and accumulate the signal so it will be steady enough for a DVM to read.

You should use a *digital* voltmeter since the output will be too low for most analog meters to show.

Use the Line Noise Meter to look at the noise on each phase. If your DVM reads 20mV or greater, the noise has enough strength is the right frequency to cause problems; however, it may not be occurring at the zero crossing. Only the Signal Strength Indicator will show that.

What Can You Find Out?

Assuming both the Line Noise Monitor and the Signal Strength Indicator show noise, notice if the noise is about the same strength on each phase. See if the noise level is steady or bounces up and down. Monitor the line for a while and see if the noise is always present.

I have seen external noise range from a steady 100mV on a single phase, to over 3 volts of very sporadic noise on all phases.

If the noise is about the same on both phases, and the level bounces up and down as you watch, there is probably some kind of problem with the NEUTRAL connection between the breaker box and the utility company's transformer. When a NEUTRAL has a bad connection, the voltage level of the neutral can wander around, creating a great deal of broadband noise. Some of it will be at 120Khz, and it will be on all phases. You may also notice the lights in the house brightening and dimming from time to time. You could try connecting the Line Noise Monitor between the NEUTRAL and a good, solid ground. If you see noise there, that's proof that you have a loose neutral. Connect the Line Noise Monitor between each noisy phase and GROUND. If you *don't* see noise there, you *know* you have a NEUTRAL problem.

Another thing that can cause variable noise on all phases is a bad connection between your NEUTRAL and ground. There may be a poor connection in the proper place, a poor ground, or multiple NEUTRAL to ground connections. (This connection is supposed to occur at only *one* place, usually at the main service entrance, and is normally *not* the responsibility of the utility company.)

If the noise is steady, and only on one phase, I would suspect a neighbor has a *very* noisy appliance, intercom (with the talk bar pressed), or baby monitor. If you have above-ground service, you can trace your AC wires back to a pole-mounted transformer and determine which houses are on the same transformer. With the Line Noise Monitor in hand, pay a friendly visit to these houses asking if you can "plug in" for a moment. After you've found the house with the highest reading, you can ask about intercoms and such.

What can you do to solve the noise problem? If you find a neighbor with noisy equipment, you can offer to replace the offending devices with better quality equipment.

If you suspect a NEUTRAL noise problem you can try calling the utility company. Tell them that you think your power is "dirty" because your lights flicker sometimes (even if they don't) and your electronic equipment keeps forgetting channels and such (even if they don't). If you try to explain the true problem, you'll get nothing but blank stares. Every utility company I've worked with steadfastly refuses to believe that anything above 60Hz can exist. Furthermore, even if it did, it's not their problem. Complain about something more understandable, however, and most utilities will send a truck to sniff around and measure things. During this process, it's common practice to "cinch" down all connections and check for used-up transformers (they *do* wear out). They may just solve your problem for you while they perform some useful "preventive maintenance" for themselves.

If you want to fix the problem yourself, and guarantee that you won't have any similar problems in the future, you can install a noise block in your breaker box or at your service entrance. Several are on the market, but I prefer the Leviton 6284 Blocking Coupler. This block works well, is much less expensive than the others, and is much easier to install (it goes in your breaker box, see Figure 19).

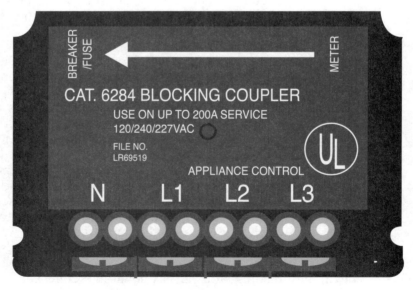

Figure 19. 6284 Blocking Coupler

One comment about noise blocks: They all tend to "soak up" some of the legitimate PLC signals. You *will* need a signal bridge, and maybe even a signal amplifier, after installing a whole-house noise block. For new construction, where extensive use of PLC devices is intended, we recommend a noise block, and either a signal bridge (if no sub-panels) or a signal amplifier in the main panel and a signal bridge in each sub-panel.

Appendix A
Test Equipment

"If an important decision is to be made, [the Persians] discuss the question when they are drunk, and the following day the master of the house where the discussion was held submits their decision for reconsideration when they are sober. If they still approve of it, it is adopted; if not, it is abandoned. Conversely, any decision they make when they are sober, is reconsidered afterwards when they are drunk."

—Herodotus, *The Histories*

If you're serious about being a PLC troubleshooter, add the following items to your toolkit, each of which is described in this chapter:

- Automatic Test Transmitter
- Signal Strength Indicator
- Test Cord
- Circuit Tester
- Mini Controller
- Remote Transceiver and 16+ Remote
- Screw-in AC Outlet

Automatic Test Transmitter

The Leviton 6385, when plugged in, transmits repeating, known level, P1-ON and P1-OFF codes. You can get by without this transmitter if you have a plug-in controller and a buddy to stand there pressing buttons all day. You can buy or rent the 6385 from your favorite home-automation retailer (see Figure 20).

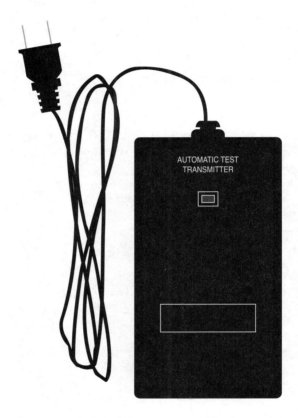

Figure 20. Leviton 6385 Automatic Test Transmitter

Signal Strength Indicator

The Leviton 6386 displays the current signal strength, from 20mV to 2V. It also has an ERROR light that tells you when you have noise on your powerline. This device is invaluable for troubleshooting PLC problems (see Figure 21).

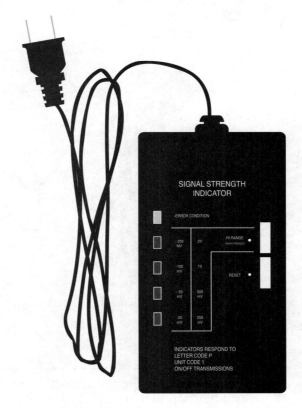

Figure 21. Leviton 6386 Signal Strength Indicator

Test Cord

The 6385 and 6386 are plug-in devices. Sometimes you will want to connect either, or both, of these devices to bare wires or terminals in your breaker box. Creating your own test cord is quick and easy. Get an extension cord (polarized connectors, but no ground) and cut off the plug end. Attach well-insulated alligator clips to each of the wires. (Radio Shack part number 270-359) Now you can plug the test set into the extension cord, and connect it to anything (see Figure 22).

Figure 22. Test cord.

 I am describing the test cord because I find this device helpful in troubleshooting some PLC problems. If you are going to use a test cord device, you should try to find one from a reputable electronic test equipment manufacturer. If you have trouble finding one, you should contact an electrician. Under no circumstances should you make or use the test cord described above if you are not a licensed electrician or electrical expert.

Circuit Tester

It's important to be able to quickly and correctly identify wires hanging out of a wall-box. It is necessary to identify LINE, NEUTRAL, GROUND, and unconnected wires when wiring wall-switches. I used to use a digital voltmeter (DVM) for this task, but this had several problems:

What could I measure the wire "against?" I had to find a neutral (through some other means) before I could measure any other wire.

If a wire measured zero volts AC, was it a neutral or not connected?

A rather insidious problem was that unconnected wires could pick up stray voltages due to the other live wires they run beside. So a disconnected wire *could* measure anywhere from zero to 120 VAC (a DVM doesn't load down the wire to measure it).

Adding a load resistor across the leads of the DVM could solve the last problem, but the other two remain. Electricians sometimes use a small handheld device that, with no physical connection, can indicate live wires. This is useful, but it still doesn't differentiate between neutral and unconnected wires (a necessity when re-wiring three- and four-way switches). A simple neon light circuit tester (Radio Shack part number 22-102, approximately $1.99) and some experience, can quickly and correctly identify wires. But it's impossible to write a "procedure" to allow the inexperienced person to do this.

There are some fairly expensive circuit testers designed to identify wires, but I have found a much less expensive solution. Figure 23 shows a circuit tester made from an "off the shelf" outlet tester (Radio Shack part number 22-101, approximately $5.99) and a polarized, ungrounded extension cord. Cut off the plastic molding on the "socket" end of the extension cord so that you can plug in the outlet tester. The socket end is molded to prevent the ground plug from entering.) To use, plug the extension cord into a live outlet near the wires you wish to test. The center (green) light will be on indicating the tester has power. Touch a wire to the ground pin and observe the result:

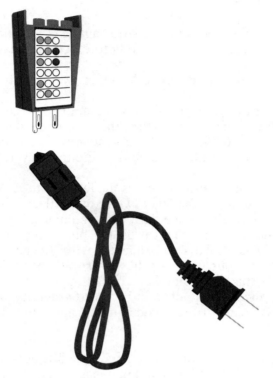

Figure 23. Circuit Tester

- If the green light turns on, the wire is a NEUTRAL or LOAD wire. (Or a ground if there is no insulation or the insulation is green).
- If the red light comes on, the wire is a LINE on the same phase as the outlet. If both the red and green lights come on, the wire is a LINE on a different phase than the outlet.
- If neither light comes on, the wire is unconnected. (If the load is connected and is lamped, this wire must be a TRAVELER. Otherwise, it could be a LOAD wire.)

We are describing the circuit tester because we find this device helpful in troubleshooting some PLC problems. If you are going to use a circuit tester, you should try to find one from a reputable electronic test equipment manufacturer. If you have trouble finding one, you should contact an electrician. Under no circumstances should you make or use the test cord described above if you are not a licensed electrician or electrical expert.

Miscellaneous Equipment

If you don't have it already, consider adding this equipment to your toolkit.

Mini-Controller

The X-10 Mini-Controller (MC460) is useful for testing the operation of modules at the location of the module. Use the Test Cord if it's a wire-in module (see Figure 24).

Figure 24. Mini Controller

Transceiver and 16+ Remote

Connect the transceiver (TM751) where a controller usually goes (use the Test Cord if necessary), and use the remote control (RT504 or 6313) to test modules around the house. This allows you to "send" the commands from where the controller is normally connected, without needing a second person or running back and forth between the controller and the module to see if it's working (see Figure 25).

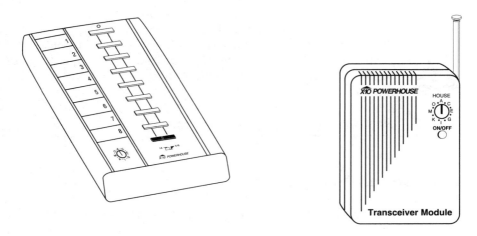

Figure 25. Wireless Transceiver and Remote Control

Screw-In AC Outlet

You may wish to measure the PLC signal strength before installing a wall-switch. This is much easier if you have a screw-in AC socket. You can screw this adapter into a lamp socket, then plug in the Signal Strength Indicator to measure the PLC signal. (Don't forget to turn the light switch on.) Note: Don't try to do this *after* you've installed the PLC switch. The switch will greatly affect the readings you get. The outlet is available at any hardware store (see Figure 26).

Figure 26. Screw-in AC Outlet

Appendix B
Concepts

"To all of these things our friends listened openmouthed—it seemed to them impossible of belief that anything so stupendous could have been devised by mortal man. That was why to Jurgis it seemed almost profanity to speak about the place as did Jokubas, skeptically: it was a thing as tremendous as the universe—the laws and ways of its working no more than the universe to be questioned or understood."

—Upton Sinclair, *The Jungle*

Overview

This appendix provides a brief overview of PowerLine Carrier (PLC) technology using X-10-compatible products. You should read this chapter if you're unfamiliar with X-10 technology.

First you'll learn about the basic components of a home-automation system: **controllers** and **modules.** Next you'll learn how controllers communicate with modules by sending **commands** to them. You'll learn about the specific commands, and how controllers send commands to particular modules by using the module's **address.**

When you've finished this chapter, you should have a solid understanding of **X-10 Home Automation** components and their operation, and you should be ready to learn about the various troubleshooting methodologies that keep a PLC system running.

Basics

You need two types of devices to automate your home: controllers and modules. Modules are adapters that you connect to light switches, lamps, appliances, or other devices that you want to control. Controllers send commands to modules to control the device attached to the module.

The diagram below shows the simplest X-10 configuration: a single controller sending commands to a single module. The controller shown here is used to turn the lamp on and off, and to dim or brighten it.

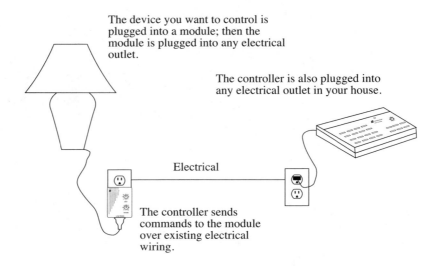

The device you want to control is plugged into a module; then the module is plugged into any electrical outlet.

The controller is also plugged into any electrical outlet in your house.

Electrical

The controller sends commands to the module over existing electrical wiring.

You can buy modules to control just about anything: lights, appliances, sprinklers, security systems—even draperies. In general, any controller can be used to control any of the modules, and we often will use the term **device** to refer generically to something that can be attached to an X-10 module. A complete description of the most popular controllers and modules is available in *Approaching Home Automation,* which is available from leading home-automation resellers.

You may be asking, "Why not just turn the lamp on and off by hand?" That's a good question. In fact, there will be times when you'll want to turn the light on and off by hand, and you'll still be able to do that once you're using X-10 controllers and modules. But if you've ever stumbled through a dark house to find a light switch, left a garage light on all night (or all week), been startled by a noise in the middle of the night, or gone on vacation and worried about your house looking empty, then an X-10 system can be an inexpensive way to make your life a whole lot easier.

At this point, you're probably thinking, "Well, that's all great, but I'll bet it's a pain in the neck to set up the system." Wrong. X-10 controllers and modules communicate over the existing electrical wiring in your home, so you don't need to install new wiring. You just plug modules and controllers into existing electrical outlets. The

X-10 devices can send commands over the same wire that carries electricity throughout the house (without disrupting your electrical service in any way, of course).

For a more in-depth discussion of the technology, see Appendix C, "Technical Overview," on page 83.

Controllers

You've already learned that there are two components to every X-10 system: controllers and modules. You also know that controllers send commands to modules and that modules execute those commands to control the devices attached to them.

When you want to control a device, you push one or more buttons on the face of the controller. (Or, if you are using the Home Automation Interface, you enter commands at your computer.) When you push a button, the controller sends a command to the module or modules that you've selected, and the modules control the devices attached to them.

This section describes the commands that controllers use to communicate with modules. There are two types of commands: **address commands** and **function commands.** Address commands identify the modules that you want to control. Function commands tell the modules what to do.

Address Commands

Each X-10 module has a specific address, which you'll learn more about in the next section. X-10 controllers use these addresses to send function commands to a particular module. This is how an X-10 controller can turn on a light in the living room without turning on every other device in the house at the same time.

When the controller sends an address command, the module or modules with that address "wake up" and begin listening for a function command. As soon as they "hear" the function command, they perform that function.

Function Commands

Here's a description of the different X-10 function commands:

ON/OFF. You can use X-10 controllers and modules to turn lights, appliances, and other devices on and off.

DIM/BRIGHT. You also can use X-10 controllers to dim incandescent lights—even lights without a dimmer control.

ALL LIGHTS ON. Some controllers allow you to turn on all of the lights in the house with a single button. This is especially useful in an emergency—for example, when you suspect that someone is breaking in. With ALL LIGHTS ON, you can turn on every light in the system at once, possibly scaring away the intruder.

ALL UNITS OFF. Controllers that support ALL LIGHTS ON also support ALL UNITS OFF. This turns off all of the devices attached to modules with the same Housecode (more about Housecodes later). ALL UNITS OFF provides a convenient way to turn off all of the lights in the house after you're in bed, or to make sure that you've turned off all appliances before leaving town.

Modules

Modules are adapters that you install between the device you want to control and the source of electricity for the device. For example, the Lamp Module is a small interface box that you plug a lamp into. Then you plug the Lamp Module into an electrical outlet. Because the Lamp Module sits between the source of electricity (the outlet) and the device (the lamp), it can control the device by regulating the amount of electricity the device receives.

Other modules replace standard light switches and control the lights that the switches turn on and off. Still others can control low-voltage electrical devices, such as lawn sprinklers and outdoor lighting.

In the previous section, we introduced the concept of the module address, which controllers use to send function commands to specific modules or groups of modules.

X-10 addresses are similar to the addresses that the post office uses to deliver mail. The post office can identify an individual house because each house has a unique address: a street number and name, a city, a state, and a zip code. X-10 addresses are a little simpler than postal addresses because they have only two components: a **Housecode** and a **Unit Code**.

You set the Housecode and Unit Code of a module by adjusting two dials on the front of the module. Typical dials are shown below.

HOUSE
CODE

UNIT
CODE

Each dial has 16 different settings. The Housecode is selected from the letters A through P, and the Unit Code is selected from the numbers 1 through 16. The address of the module is simply its Housecode followed by its Unit Code. So, for example, the address of the module shown above is A1.

Because there are 16 different Housecodes and 16 different Unit Codes, there are (16 x 16) 256 possible addresses. That should be more than enough for the average home. You also can assign two or more modules the same address if you want to control them simultaneously. For example, you might have two porch lights that you want to go on and off at the same time. In that case, you can assign both modules the same address.

In general, you can assign addresses to modules however you want, but there are some guidelines that you might want to follow to make your system easier to use. Here are a few suggestions here.

• Select devices that you *always* want to control at the same time and give them the same address (the same Unit Code and Housecode).

By assigning the same address to all of the modules in a group, you are able to turn all of them on or off simply by pushing a single button on the controller. In addition, you can create **timed events** to control all of these modules with an X-10 Mini Timer or an X-10 Home Automation Interface (CP-290).

• Select devices that you *occasionally* want to control simultaneously and give them the same Housecode.

This allows you to control the group of devices with the ALL LIGHTS ON and ALL UNITS OFF commands. For example, you might have 10 different lights in your home. By giving all of them the same Housecode, you can turn off all of them at night from a single controller on your nightstand. But, at the same time, you might have other devices—for example, a stereo or an outdoor porch light—that you *don't* want to turn off when you go to bed. In that case, you assign these lights and appliances a *different* Housecode from that for the rest of the lights so that the ALL UNITS OFF command would not turn them off.

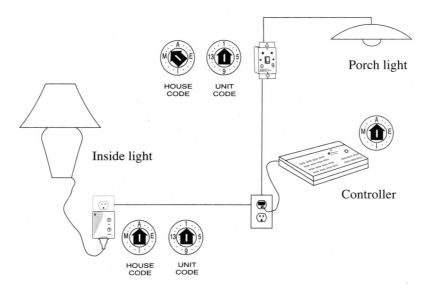

In the diagram above, the ALL UNITS OFF button on the controller turns off the inside light, but not the porch light. That's because the porch light has a different Housecode.

Also, the buttons on a controller send commands to only one Housecode. You must adjust a dial on the controller to send commands to modules with a different Housecode. By grouping modules with similar functions, you can control the entire group with a single controller. For example, if you have five sprinkler heads in the yard and 10 lights in the house, you could have one controller next to your bed for controlling all lights and another on the porch for controlling all sprinklers.

Compatibility

The set of commands described in this chapter, and the method for transmitting them over standard electrical wire, were established in the late 1970s by a company named X-10 (USA), Inc. Literally thousands of X-10–compatible home-automation products are in use today.

Appendix C
Technical Overview

"The man who, being really on the Way, falls upon hard times in the world will not, as a consequence, turn to that friend who offers him refuge and comfort and encourages his old self to survive. Rather, he will seek out someone who will faithfully and inexorably help him to risk himself, so that he may endure the suffering and pass courageously through, thus making of it a 'raft that leads to the far shore.'"

—Karlfried Graf von Durckheim, *The Way of Transformation*.

Overview

You don't really need to refer to this appendix when designing, installing, and troubleshooting X-10 systems. Rather, this appendix provides a basic understanding of how X-10 works, and is targeted at the more curious troubleshooter.

How It Works

X-10 is based on a technology broadly called **Power Line Carrier.** As you have seen, this design is based on the concept of using the existing transport mechanism for electricity—the AC power lines in your home—to carry the commands that controllers send and modules receive. The most obvious benefit of this technology is that there's no need for additional wiring, which can be a huge obstacle in automating existing homes. Power Line Carrier systems also draw the power necessary for the signal—a tiny amount— directly from the power line that is used as the transport mechanism. No alternate power or transformer is required.

All of this takes place with no noticeable effect on the power line itself. The signals are sent back and forth at a frequency that's much higher than that of the electrical current. Appliances and lights that are not connected to X-10 modules never know the difference. The exceptions are other devices that use the same system to transmit signals, such as certain home intercom systems. Problems can occur if the intercom uses frequencies in the same bandwidth as X-10. Most manufacturers attempt to avoid this problem because the X-10 standard is well-established.

Household wiring is subject to **noise** on the line from appliances, fluorescent lights, electric motors, televisions, and other items that create electrical noise while operating. This limits the amount of information that can be transmitted effectively in this manner.

For systems such as X-10, the amount of data sent is actually quite small. The signal is sent in one-millisecond bursts of 120 kHz. The information is sent at the **zero crossing point** of the 60-Hz frequency of electrical power (see Figure 27). A 120-kHz signal at the zero crossing point represents a **binary** "1," and the lack of a signal at the zero crossing point represents a binary "0."

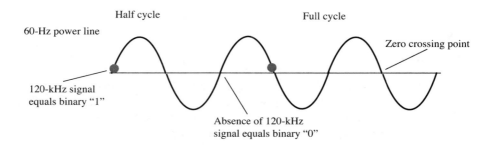

Figure 27. Zero Crossing Point

You might think of this as an inaudible Morse code signal traveling across your electrical wires.

When a module "hears" the **Start Code**—1110—come across the line, it knows that the next signal will be the Housecode. If the next thing that the module hears is its own preset Housecode, it listens to the next four signals, or bits, to find out if its unique Unit Code is being sent. If it hears that code (represented by Unit Code 1 through 16 on each module), it is ready to act on the next code sent, which is the five-bit Function Code. If another Housecode or Unit Code comes across the line at any point in the sequence, the module recognizes that the message is meant for another module and stops listening. This entire sequence is shown graphically in Figure 28.

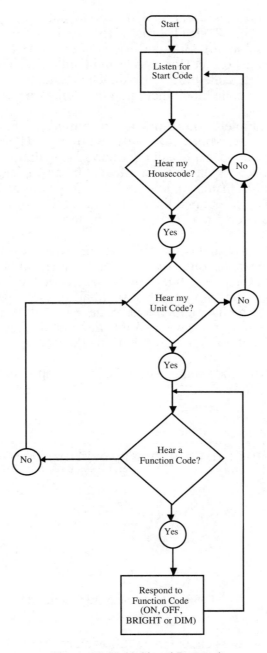

Figure 28. X-10 Signal Processing

The complete transmission of the X-10 code requires 11 cycles of the power line. The first two cycles represent the Start Code, the next

four cycles represent the Housecode, and the last five represent
either a Unit Code (1 through 16) or a Function Code (ON, OFF,
DIM, and so on). Modules listen to Function Codes only if they have
received a correct Housecode and Unit Code. The order is critical—
a complete code block with the Unit Code first, followed by a
complete code block including the Function Code.

Each complete code block is transmitted twice, with three clear (no
signal) power-line cycles between pairs. BRIGHT and DIM
Function Codes are sent continuously, with no cycles separating
them, because they are, in effect, "increasing" or "decreasing"
commands instead of single ON or OFF commands. For example, if
BRIGHT is sent and the next code is DIM, or Unit Code 1, then a
three-power-line-cycle gap will be left.

Each bit or signal is actually transmitted twice—once in its true form
and once in its complement, or opposite, form on the next half of the
cycle of the power line. This helps ensure the accuracy of the
signals. If any signal on the first half of the power cycle is not
followed by its complement on the next half of the power signal, it
is ignored. This is a very simple method of error checking that helps
ensure that your modules don't respond to line noise.

The entire code sequence, including complements, is shown in
Figure 29.

Start Code	H1 $\overline{H1}$	H2 $\overline{H2}$	H4 $\overline{H4}$	H8 $\overline{H8}$	D1 $\overline{D1}$	D2 $\overline{D2}$	D4 $\overline{D4}$	D8 $\overline{D8}$	D16 $\overline{D16}$
1110	1 0	0 1	1 0	1 0	0 1	0 1	0 1	1 0	1 0
1110	1	0	1	1	0	0	0	1	1

Figure 29. Sample X-10 Command Sequence

Each signal, such as H1, is followed by its complement, $\overline{H1}$. If
H1=1—meaning that a 120-kHz signal was detected at the crossing
point of the 60-Hz power line, and on the next half cycle another
120-kHz signal was detected—a transmission error (no
complement) would be detected, and the entire code sequence would
be ignored. The exception to this rule is the Start Code, which is
always the unique 1110. Because no complement is necessary for

the Start Code, four bits of information can be sent in two cycles of the power line (one bit per half cycle, with no complement). The next bit requires a full cycle for the signal on the first half and the complement on the second half.

Each complete 11-cycle code block (Start Code, Housecode, and Function or Address Code) is sent twice to double the chances that the code is received correctly. The two types of redundancy (sending the complement bit and sending the complete code block twice) are a simple yet effective way of ensuring signal accuracy and transmission without requiring a "return signal" from the modules, which would require additional hardware and dramatically increase cost.

Table 4 lists code sequences for Address Commands.

Table 4: Code Sequences for Address Commands

	Housecodes					Unit Codes				
	H1	H2	H4	H8		D1	D2	D4	D8	D16
A	0	1	1	0	**1**	0	1	1	0	0
B	1	1	1	0	**2**	1	1	1	0	0
C	0	0	1	0	**3**	0	0	1	0	0
D	1	0	1	0	**4**	1	0	1	0	0
E	0	0	0	1	**5**	0	0	0	1	0
F	1	0	0	1	**6**	1	0	0	1	0
G	0	1	0	1	**7**	0	1	0	1	0
H	1	1	0	1	**8**	1	1	0	1	0
I	0	1	1	1	**9**	0	1	1	1	0
J	1	1	1	1	**10**	1	1	1	1	0
K	0	0	1	1	**11**	0	0	1	1	0
L	1	0	1	1	**12**	1	0	1	1	0
M	0	0	0	0	**13**	0	0	0	0	0
N	1	0	0	0	**14**	1	0	0	0	0
O	0	1	0	0	**15**	0	1	0	0	0
P	1	1	0	0	**16**	1	1	0	0	0

Table 5 lists code sequences for Function Commands.

Table 5: Code Sequences for Function Commands

Function Command	Code Sequence				
ALL UNITS OFF	0	0	0	0	1
ALL LIGHTS ON	0	0	0	1	1
ON	0	0	1	1	1
OFF	0	0	1	1	1
DIM	0	1	0	0	1
BRIGHT	0	1	0	1	1
ALL LIGHTS OFF	0	1	1	0	1

The X-10 code format is patented, but there are ways to use the technology for your own product ideas without dealing with complicated licensing issues. If you're interested in developing your own X-10–compatible products, we suggest that you investigate two products available from X-10 (USA), Inc., for OEM manufacturers and hobbyists: the PL513 transmitter and the TW523 transmitter/receiver. Both products plug into regular AC outlets and use a standard telephone RJ-11 interface to connect to your product or experiment. This method eliminates the need to connect directly to 110 AC current and makes implementation safer and easier.

If you want more information about the technical aspects of X-10 technology and more sophisticated aspects of home automation, you can refer to *Circuit Cellar* magazine or call X-10 (USA).

Appendix D
Sources

This Appendix includes a list of the firms whose products are mentioned throughout the book.

Approaching, Inc.

1055 Fairview Avenue
San Jose, CA 95125
Inquiries: (408) 335-0957
Orders: (800) 356-6954
www.approaching.com

Leviton Manufacturing Company, Inc.

59-25 Little Neck Parkway
Little Neck, NY 11362
Phone: (718) 281-6488
Fax: (718) 631-6508

Radio Shack Plug 'n Power

700 One Tandy Center
Fort Worth, TX 76102
Phone: (817) 878-4852
Fax: (817) 878-6508

X-10 (USA), Inc.

91 Ruckman Road
Closter, NJ 07624-0420
Phone: (201) 784-9700

Please note that this list only includes information on products discussed in this book. However, there are many companies that make X-10-compatible equipment. For an extensive list of sources for X-10-compatible equipment, pick up a copy of Approaching, Inc.'s best-selling *Approaching Home Automation, A Guide to Using X-10 Technologies,* available at most home automation equipment resellers or through Approaching, Inc. at the number listed above. For information on this or other Approaching, Inc. publications, visit our web site at www.approaching.com.

Glossary

address
The combination of a module's Housecode and Unit Code—for example, A1.

address commands
Commands that a controller sends to identify modules before sending function commands. The address command consists of a Housecode and a Unit Code. After receiving the address command, modules with that Housecode and Unit Code listen for subsequent function commands, which they execute.

binary
A numbering system made up of only 1s and 0s that is used by computer systems and electrical devices.

circuit breaker
A safety switch in your wiring that turns off the electricity to a certain portion of your home if a problem occurs that increases the amount of current beyond the circuit breaker's rated capacity.

commands
Messages that a controller sends to a module to control it. See also **address commands** and **function commands.**

CONTROL
The wire that provides the signal from the slave switch to the master in a 3-way or 4-way switched circuit.

controller
A device that sends address commands and function commands telling a module what function to perform. Many types of controllers are available, including the Maxi Controller, the Mini Controller, the programmable Mini Timer, and the Home Automation Interface, which works in conjunction with a computer. They all have special features that provide a variety of ways to send address and function commands to modules.

cutoff switch
A device that physically breaks a circuit, making sure that electricity doesn't flow.

device
A generic term for an entity controlled by an X-10 module—for example, a lamp or an appliance.

fluorescent

A bulb that creates light by exciting a gas contained in a pressurized tube. Fluorescent bulbs are usually long and thin and produce very little heat. They can be turned on and off by an Appliance Module, but never should be used with a Lamp Module. Fluorescent lights cannot be dimmed.

function command

A command that a controller sends to a module after it has identified the module with an address command. Modules respond to all function commands until they receive another, different address command.

Housecode

A letter from A through O that's used to identify groups of modules. The Housecode and the Unit Code of a module together make up the module's address. Housecodes provide a useful way of grouping modules; for example, all modules with the same Housecode respond to the ALL LIGHTS ON and ALL UNITS OFF commands.

incandescent

A bulb that creates light by forcing electricity through a filament. Incandescent bulbs produce heat. They can be controlled by a Lamp Module, turned on and off, and dimmed.

LINE

The hot, or live, wire that carries unswitched AC current to the switch.

LOAD

The device that uses electricity and thus places a "load" on the circuit. Examples are lamps, appliances, and motors.

main panel

The circuit breaker that takes electricity from the utility company source and distributes it to multiple home circuits.

module

An interface box that you connect to lamps, appliances, or other devices to control them. Every module has an address, not necessarily unique, that consists of a Housecode and a Unit Code. Controllers communicate with modules by sending addresses and commands to them.

noise

Random high-frequency electrical signals that travel over the power line created by sources not used for X-10 signalling.

Power Line Carrier (PLC)
A system that uses existing AC power lines for the transmission of control signals from controllers to remote modules. Power Line Carrier systems superimpose signals in a frequency that doesn't interfere with the transmission of power, and they don't require additional wiring.

radio frequency
A transmission method that uses high-frequency waves for signaling. Radio frequency signals can penetrate walls and glass (depending on power levels) and don't require the receiver to be within the line of sight.

Start Code
The special signal that lets a module know that the next signal coming is the Housecode. The X-10 Start Code is 1110.

sub-panel
A secondary distribution system for electricity that divides a large feed from the main panel into multiple circuits.

TLA
Three-Letter Acronym.

timed event
A command that's stored in the controller and sent to modules at a specified time. Timed events can take place just once or can recur on certain days of the week.

travelers
The wires that only connect the switches in a 3-way or 4-way switched wiring system. These wires never connect directly to the load. Depending on the status of the switches, these wires may carry line-voltage or be floating (unconnected).

triac
The mechanism inside an electronic switch used to control the load.

Unit Code
A number from 1 through 16 that is used to differentiate modules. The Housecode and the Unit Code of a module together make up the module's address.

watt
A measurement of the quantity of electrical current that flows through a circuit.

X-10 Home Automation
Home-automation technology that uses controllers and modules to communicate over existing electrical wiring. X-10 technology is inexpensive, flexible, and easy to use.

zero crossing point
The midpoint of the amplitude of an AC sine wave. This is where X-10 signals are sent.

Index

test cord 14, 70
traveler 31
triac 2
TW523 transmitter/receiver 88

U

Unit Codes, about 80

V

voltage tester 36
voltmeter 32

W

wired hot fixtures 54

X

X-10 controllers
    CP290 19, 27
    MC460 19
    MT522 19, 27
    PF284 19
    RT504 74
    SC503 19
    SD533 19
    TM751 74
    TR551 19
    TW523 19
X-10 modules
    AM466 19, 26, 59
    AM486 19, 26, 59
    little brown modules 2, 27
    LM465 2, 12, 19, 26, 59
    PR511 3
    RR501 13
    SC503 12
    SC546 19
    SL575 26
    SR227 26
    TM751 3, 13
    UM506 19
    WS467 2, 3, 5, 12
    WS477 2, 5, 7
    WS4777 12, 36–38, 45–46
X-10 transceivers
    RR501 19
    TM751 19
X-10–compatible products 82

Z

zero crossing point 11, 84